# STAR WARS

## EPISODE I

### THE VISUAL DICTIONARY

*Sensor implant*

*Long fingers to draw blood*

*Tracker utility vest*

*Short-range pistol*

*Protective body paint*

*Long-range projectile rifle*

*Heavy leather boots for desert travel*

AURRA SING

Field generator
confines bird

Optional data-feed
package

Full-read-out display

PODRACE FAN'S
MACROBINOCULARS

Display crest

Engineer's name,
"Jabesq", in Naboo
Futhork

Pylat bird

NEIMOIDIAN
BIRD CAGE

Sound-damping
layers

NABOO HANGAR CHIEF
ENGINEER'S HELMET

Manual start
knob

Simple ionizer
array

Heat radiator
shroud

Display confirms
transmission of
door entry code

Complex
ionizer array

Sand-tight
construction

TATOOINE GUNMAN'S BLASTER

GYRDA KEYPAD

Charge generator
assembly

Sweeper screen stabilizes
local fields for delicate
maintenance

Antenna for
communication
with Theed Palace
computer system

Spinner motor

Cooling
unit

HANGAR DECK
SCRUBBER DROID

Stereo sniffers find
drops of dangerous
leaked fuel

WATTO'S IONIZER

Sunshield
fabric

MOS ESPA COOLTH BACKPACK

Monocular navigation
photoreceptor

Fuel scrubbers
(on underside)

JEDI LIGHTSABRE

Cycling field generators

*Single antenna*

COMLINK

# STAR WARS®

## EPISODE I
### THE VISUAL DICTIONARY

BLISSL TUNER
(MUSICAL INSTRUMENT)

Written by
DAVID WEST REYNOLDS

*Afterburner*

*Fuel lines*

*Lubricant hose*

*Absurdly heavy load*

*Pit droid near collapse*

*Lead pit droid*

PIT DROIDS CARRYING PODRACER ENGINE

*Emitter assembly*

LUCAS BOOKS

DK

DORLING KINDERSLEY
LONDON • NEW YORK • STUTTGART • MOSCOW • SYDNEY

SLAVE QUARTERS
BRAZIER

# Contents

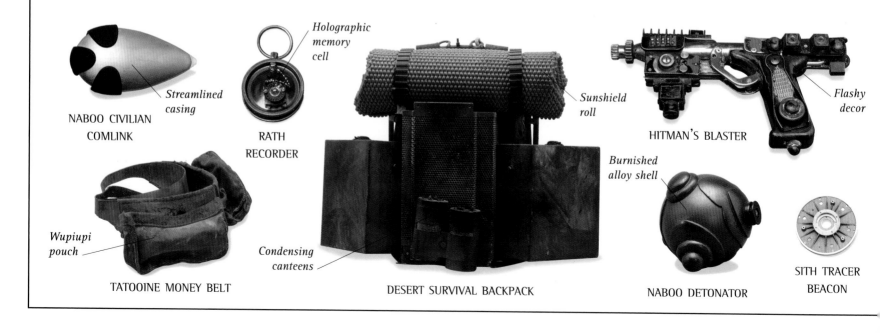

Streamlined casing

NABOO CIVILIAN COMLINK

Holographic memory cell

RATH RECORDER

Sunshield roll

Wupiupi pouch

Condensing canteens

TATOOINE MONEY BELT

DESERT SURVIVAL BACKPACK

Flashy decor

HITMAN'S BLASTER

Burnished alloy shell

NABOO DETONATOR

SITH TRACER BEACON

# Introduction

EPISODE I travels back to the beginning of the *Star Wars* saga, a generation before Luke Skywalker meets Ben Kenobi and sets out on his path to destiny. In this era, Luke Skywalker's father Anakin is nine years old, and the great free Galactic Republic still stands, although its power is starting to falter. This time is populated with new characters, whose worlds are replete with gleaming spacecraft, intricate clothing and exotic-looking robots. Just as in the real world, these artifacts tell a story. They are clues to identity. From the deathly pale appearance of Trade Federation battle droids to the tasty gorgs of Mos Espa marketplace and the fangs of the colo claw fish, the Visual Dictionary is your guide to the dazzling worlds explored in this new episode of the *Star Wars* fantasy. Because even at the beginning, there's a lot to catch up on. So jump on board.

And brace yourself.

NABOO ROYAL
STARSHIP

*Hooded cloak*

*Hidden visage*

*Sith clasp*

# The Phantom Menace

Founded LONG AGO, the Republic has united countless thousands of star systems under a single, far-reaching government. In millennia past, great sections of the Republic fought each other even as they clung to threads of unity. Peace and justice came to prevail under the protection of the wise and powerful Jedi, who draw on a mystical power known as the Force. Through the guidance of the Galactic Senate, civilization grew and the Republic became prosperous. But the price of comfort was weakness. The institutions of government became decadent and Jedi numbers dwindled to a mere 10,000. Now, the Force itself is unbalanced and great change seems imminent...

## Coruscant

A world enveloped in a single city, Coruscant is the home of galactic government and the effective center of the known universe. Representatives from all member worlds congregate here to participate in the colossal enterprise of galactic government. From among the thousands within the senate chamber, the pleas of a single voice must be heard to save the small planet of Naboo from invasion.

On Coruscant, the leadership of the Galactic Senate is served by the Jedi – guardians of peace and justice in the Galaxy. It is on the decisions and actions of the Jedi High Council that the fate of the galaxy will turn as the forces of darkness begin to gather their strength.

## Darth Sidious

The Sith Lord Darth Sidious sets into motion the final stages of his order's 2,000-year-old plan to destroy the Jedi. Working patiently, Sidious has extended his power and influence deep into the galactic government. Using his grasp of psychology and bureaucracy to stifle justice, he brings about the crisis he needs to make his move for domination.

Coruscant provides a hiding place for the mysterious Sith. This ancient dark order has been waiting in the shadows, preparing to prey upon the Galactic Republic's time of weakness and usher in a new era of Sith rule. This phantom menace radiates outwards from the centre, drawing into its web individuals and worlds that lie far beyond Coruscant.

# Naboo

*Theed Royal Palace*    *Palace forecourt*    *Naboo philosophers*

The provincial and little-populated planet of Naboo has benefited greatly from membership in the Republic. Within an idyll of serenity, Naboo decorative architecture expresses the planet's philosophy of arts and a harmonious way of life. The Naboo have come to regard their privilege as a birthright and do not realize the extent to which they are dependent on the core strength of galactic government to protect them. Only when crisis descends will they face the frightening realization that the only strength they can depend on is their own.

Expressive of Naboo style in its glistening silver finish and dreamlike, artful contours, the Royal Starship is nonetheless built around a core of foreign-made engine systems. Naboo society is similarly dependent on outside industry.

*Hydrostatic bubbles keep out water*

*Gungan-style artistic floor pattern*

*Overload burnout scar*    *Area of field leakage*    *Naboo-made charge planes*

## Otoh Gunga

Removed from outside contact, the underwater Gungan cities of Naboo glisten like scintillating jewellery. The Gungan capital city, Otoh Gunga, prides itself on being independent of foreign influences. Nonetheless, it relies upon a quiet but vital trade with the Naboo. In this, as in the danger they face from the Trade Federation, the Gungans find that they are more connected with outsiders than they confess.

*Typical Gungan design*

*Core chamber holds Nubian T-14 generator*

*Hyperdrive effect channels improve supralight performance*

*Slave quarters*    *Rough adobe walls*

# Hyperdrive Core

A dazzling example of Naboo style, the hyperdrive core of the Royal Starship is an intricate maze of charge planes and effect channels that allows the ship to slip smoothly beyond lightspeed. When the Nubian-made hyperdrive generator inside the core fails under the energy overloads encountered in battle, the Naboo begin to learn the realities of their dependence on the outside world.

TOUCHDOWN ON TATOOINE
The Naboo Royal Starship is forced by the broken hyperdrive core to land on the desert world of Tatooine. Queen Amidala must seek refuge in this wilderness and stake her hopes on desperate chance.

# Tatooine

Beyond the reach of the Republic are the worlds of the Outer Rim, a frontier where extremes of freedom and slavery coexist. Tatooine is ruled by wealthy trading barons and gangsters. The adobe architecture of Mos Espa looks as rugged and primitive as the planet itself, but the thick walls hide sophisticated interior cooling systems. On Tatooine, not everything is what it seems – as those aboard the Naboo Royal Starship find when they encounter a slave boy named Anakin Skywalker.

# Mace Windu

THE WISDOM and self-sacrifice of Mace Windu, senior member of the Jedi Council, is legendary. In a long and adventurous career, he has repeatedly risked his life to resolve great conflicts in fairness to both sides. Windu is sober and cool-minded but is also capable of dramatic actions in the face of danger. Even experienced Jedi look to this great man in times of serious trouble. Always ready to risk himself, Mace Windu is reluctant to risk the lives of others. In particular, he is wary of fellow Jedi Qui-Gon Jinn's headstrong belief in Anakin Skywalker, and senses great danger with the boy. These concerns weigh heavily upon him as he considers them against his friendship and respect for Qui-Gon.

Time and again, Mace Windu has stood at the centre of great conflicts. His fame has only added to his negotiating skills.

Under-tunic

Tunic

Jedi robe

Utility belt

Lightsabre

Deflector shield generator

Docking ring

Crew lounge

Colour indicates diplomatic status

Cockpit

Diplomatic salon pod

## Republic Cruiser

Jedi, diplomats and ambassadors travel to trouble spots around the galaxy aboard the Republic Cruiser. The vessel's striking red colour declares its political neutrality. In its armoured salon pods, high-level negotiations take place between factions in conflict.

The Jedi High Council is secretly called upon by Supreme Chancellor Valorum of the Galactic Senate to settle the conflict with the Trade Federation. Mace Windu summons a pair of his most able Jedi for the mission. Windu little suspects the evil and danger awaiting Jedi Master Qui-Gon Jinn and his apprentice Obi-Wan Kenobi within the Trade Federation fleet.

Blade projection plate

Blade modulation circuitry

Handgrip ridges

Activator

Blade length adjust

Radiator casing segment

MACE WINDU'S LIGHTSABRE

## DATA FILE

◆ The Jedi use the lightsabre as a symbol of their dedication to combat in defence, not attack, and of their philosophical concern for finely tuned mind and body skills.

◆ Ambassadors, mediators and counsellors, Jedi are warriors only as a last resort.

# Yoda

WELL INTO HIS 800s, Yoda is the oldest member of the Jedi High Council, as well as its most deeply perceptive Master. A great traveller in his younger years, Yoda has quietly visited hundreds of worlds on his own, spending years learning different lifeways and appreciating the infinitely variable nuances of the Force. His experiences have made him cautious and reflective. Yoda takes a personal interest in the progress of Qui-Gon Jinn and his apprentice Obi-Wan Kenobi. Yoda recognizes their considerable strength and potential even as he disagrees with some of their "dangerously reckless" choices.

## Testing Screen

The Jedi High Council use multi-function viewscreens to test Jedi apprentices. These screens are built without buttons and are operated by Jedi mind powers. Only Force-attuned individuals can follow the high-speed series of images generated on screen. Testing screens keep the Jedi Council members in constant practice with their Force abilities.

The Jedi draw their power from the Force, an omnipresent, subtle energy field surrounding all living things. The Force can lend telekinetic powers and give insights into the future, the past or the thoughts of others.

Tension band indicator

Testing screen displays transmitted or recorded information

Control probe

Standard tests stored in memory cell

Blade emitter shroud

Activator matrix

YODA'S LIGHTSABRE

Power cell

Memory cap

Handgrip

Test results are recorded in removable memory cell

Sensitive ears

Well-worn Jedi robe

REVERSE VIEW

Custom-made Council seat

Having seen so much of life, Yoda views all that happens with a long perspective. Less active now than in his younger years, Yoda remains one of the two most important voices of wisdom on the Jedi High Council along with Mace Windu.

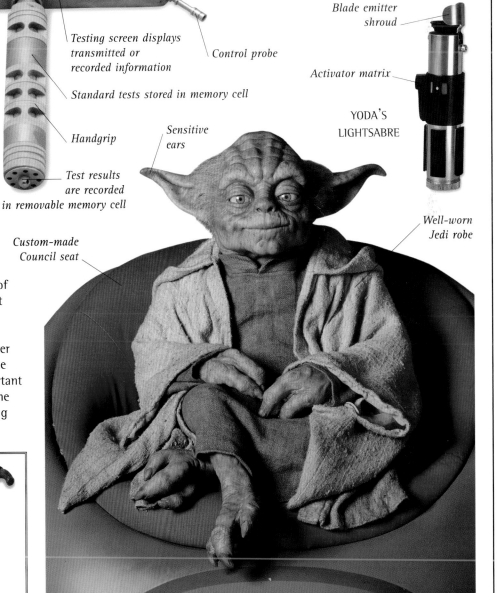

## DATA FILE

◆ Yoda's gimer stick cane helps him to walk long distances and contains natural plant substances that aid meditation when chewed.

◆ It has been many years since Yoda has needed to wield his special lightsabre. Yoda takes quiet satisfaction in finding non-violent solutions.

# The Jedi High Council

THE TWELVE MEMBERS of the Jedi High Council represent a gathering of great minds who have proven themselves and their abilities in the service of peace and justice. Confident in their attunement to the Force, the Council members work together in trust, free from the petty constraints of ego and jealousy. Their Council Chamber is a place of open thought and speech, a realm of mutual respect and a haven of shared noble purpose. The Council is composed of five permanent members who have accepted a lifetime commitment to the difficult work of the Jedi. In addition, four long-term members serve until they choose to step down and three limited-term members sit for specified terms. This balance of membership keeps the Council wise and vigorous.

*Large ears sensitive in thin atmosphere*

*Jedi topknot*

**EVEN PIELL**
Jedi Master Even Piell bears a scar across his eye as a grisly trophy of a victory against terrorists who made the mistake of underestimating the diminutive Jedi Master.

The Council Chamber is located atop the central spire of the Jedi Temple on the galactic capital planet, Coruscant. The 12 members sit in a ring of chairs that are spaced equally around the chamber.

## Yarael Poof

*Quermian upper brain*

*Well-developed horns*

The attenuated Quermian Yarael Poof is the consummate master of Jedi mind tricks. He uses Force suggestions to bring conflicts to an abrupt end, turning combatants' own fears against themselves.

*Quermians are noseless as they smell with olfactory organs in their hands*

*Customary humanoid Jedi robes*

*Long neck for peering above low vegetation mats*

*Robe hides second set of arms and chest with lower brain*

*Traditional Quermian cannom collar*

*Tough skin impervious to high winds of Iktotchon*

*Large brain supported by second heart*

## Saesee Tiin

An Iktotchi pilot, Saesee Tiin is best able to focus while travelling at extremely high speeds – at the controls of the finest spacecraft. He offers a unique perspective on the Council as his telepathic mind is always racing ahead to foresee possibilities.

*Surcoat adapted from ancient Cerean garb*

*Lightsabre*

*Cerean cuffs*

*Plain trousers*

## Ki-Adi-Mundi

A Jedi Knight from the largely unspoiled paradise world of Cerea, Ki-Adi-Mundi's high-domed head holds a complex binary brain. Recently added to the Council, Ki-Adi-Mundi has not yet taken a Padawan learner.

**EETH KOTH**

*Vestigial horn patterns identify races of Iridonian Zabrak*

Iridonian Zabrak such as Eeth Koth are renowned for their mental discipline, which allows them to tolerate great physical suffering. This ability is born of surviving their harsh homeworld.

*Tholoth headdress*

*Dense hair deters biting cygnats of Thisspias*

**OPPO RANCISIS**

Abdicating his throne on Thisspias, Oppo Rancisis instead sought to serve the entire galaxy among the Jedi order based on Coruscant. When negotiations fail, Rancisis ensures that Jedi-counselled military tactics are cunning and effective.

*Mark of illumination*

**DEPA BILLABA**

Adopting the traditional culture of Chalacta to honour her slain parents, Depa Billaba offers an ordered perspective to the wide-ranging minds of the Council.

*Utility pouch*

*Tall travel boots*

# Adi Gallia

Born into a highly placed diplomatic family stationed on Coruscant, the intuitive Adi Gallia often seems to know what people are about to say. Gallia has many contacts throughout the Coruscant political machine, making her one of the Supreme Chancellor's most valuable intelligence sources.

*Jedi robe*

*Adi's second lightsabre replaces her first, which was destroyed on a mission*

*Protective goggles*

*Antiox mask*

*Highly developed extrasensory organs*

**PLO KOON**

A Kel Dor from Dorin, Plo Koon must protect his sensitive eyes and nostrils from the oxygen-rich atmosphere of Coruscant with special devices.

*Youthful topknot*

# Yaddle

Young at only 477, Jedi Master Yaddle looks up to Yoda while leading the Council with compassion and balanced patience. Yaddle silently waits in discussions before offering her single, powerful, softly spoken comment.

## DATA FILE

◆ The 12 High Council members reflect a mere nint of the diversity within the Jedi ranks, which include members of hundreds of species and cultures.

◆ Of the teeming trillions of species that populate the galaxy, very few individuals become fully fledged Jedi Knights: the ranks based on Coruscant number only about 10,000.

# Qui-Gon Jinn
## JEDI MASTER

JEDI BLOOD
TEST KIT

MASTER QUI-GON JINN is an experienced Jedi who has proven his value to the leadership of the Jedi order in many important missions and difficult negotiations. In his maturity, however, he remains as restless as he was in his youth. When Qui-Gon encounters young Anakin Skywalker on the Outer Rim desert world of Tatooine, the Jedi is deeply struck by an unshakeable sense that the boy is part of the galaxy's destiny. In boldly championing the cause of Anakin, Qui-Gon sets in motion momentous events that will ultimately bring balance to the Force – but not without great cost.

On the desert planet of Tatooine, Qui-Gon wishes to avoid being recognized as a Jedi. Accordingly, he trades his customary Jedi robe for a rough-spun poncho such as those worn by local settlers and moisture farmers.

**REPUBLIC CRUISER**
Dispatched by the Supreme Chancellor of the Galactic Senate to settle the Trade Federation dispute, Qui-Gon travels on board the diplomatic vessel *Radiant VII*.

As the *Radiant VII* prepares to land within the Trade Federation flagship's hangar, navigation read-outs ensure precise manoeuvres.

Orientation grids

Neimoidian flagship

**DESTINATION NAVISPHERE**

Mode indicator

Trajectory path shows route ahead

Radiant VII

## Lightsabre

Following the custom of his day, Qui-Gon has built a lightsabre with a highly elaborate internal design. Multiple small power cells are stored in the scalloped handgrip and microscopic circuitry governs the nature of the energy blade. Simpler lightsabre designs, built outside the halls of the Jedi Temple on Coruscant, typically use a single large power cell inside a solid handgrip.

Qui-Gon has risen to great prominence within the Jedi order, and is well-known to the members of the High Council. Yet in spite of his outstanding service as a Jedi Knight and Master, Qui-Gon has been passed by for a seat on the Council. This is due to his bold, headstrong nature and his favouring of risk and action, which sometimes bring him into disagreement with his Jedi peers and elders.

Long hair worn back to keep vision clear

Jedi robe

Jedi tunic

Blade projection plate

Activator

Series of micro-cells

Charging port

QUI-GON JINN'S
LIGHTSABRE

Rugged travel boots

Reception
antenna

Voice pickup

Frequency
search
control

Encoding
selector

Inert
plaeklite
casing

Silence
projectors

Sound
reproduction
matrix

## Holoprojector

One of the utility devices that Qui-Gon carries is a small holoprojector. This can be tuned with a comlink to carry a hologram transmission for face-to-face contact, or it can be used as an independent image recorder and projector.

Qui-Gon loads his holoprojector with selected images from the technical databanks on board the Naboo Royal Starship. He intends to use them to help obtain repair parts when the ship is grounded on Tatooine.

*Tines rotate downward to plug into signal feed or to link to larger image projector*

Casing ring

Sturdy construction
for field use

Projection
platform

## Comlink

Qui-Gon's miniature comlink allows him to keep in touch with Obi-Wan Kenobi when the two operate separately. It features complex security devices to prevent unauthorized interception and is unlabelled to thwart use by non-Jedi. A silence projector lends privacy to conversations and helps Qui-Gon maintain stealth in the field.

COMLINK
REVERSE VIEW

On meeting Anakin, Qui-Gon believes he has recognized the prophesied individual who will restore balance and harmony to the Force. The Jedi feels so strongly that he has recognized this individual that he is not persuaded otherwise by members of the Jedi High Council, including the influential Yoda, who sense danger in the boy.

TOYDARIAN TROUBLE
Some species are naturally immune to the Jedi mind tricks of all but the most powerful Masters. Qui-Gon Jinn has never even heard of a Toydarian before he encounters Watto on Tatooine and the Jedi soon finds that he needs more than Force-assisted "suggestions" to persuade the hovering junk dealer to cooperate with him.

Qui-Gon earned the rank of Master when he trained his first Padawan apprentice to Knighthood, although his second apprentice failed to become a Knight. Obi-Wan is Qui-Gon's third Padawan and a worthy student of his wisdom and skill.

On Tatooine, Qui-Gon battles a Sith warrior wielding a deadly lightsabre. Since lightsabres are seldom handled by non-Jedi, the order primarily uses them as defence against blaster bolts rather than other lightsabres. However, lightsabre duelling is taught as part of classical Jedi training.

Hook for sliding
down cables

Liquid cable
reservoir

Grappling
spike
launcher

Dual-strand
liquid-cable
rotator

Spinner
tip

JEDI FIELD GEAR

## DATA FILE

◆ The Jedi workshops on Coruscant supply exquisite materials and tools for initiates constructing their own lightsabres. The initiates' ability to do this successfully proves their developed sensitivity to the Force.

◆ Greed and political scheming are weakening the Galactic Republic that Qui-Gon serves. In an attempt to restore lasting peace and security to the galaxy, Qui-Gon is motivated to take a more active role than that traditionally taken by the Jedi.

# Obi-Wan Kenobi
## JEDI KNIGHT

Short hair of a
Padawan apprentice

Tunic

Hooded robe

Apprentice's long braid

OBI-WAN KENOBI has followed a responsible path on his journey toward Jedi knighthood as the Padawan apprentice to Jedi Master Qui-Gon Jinn. Strongly influenced by other leading Jedi as well as by Qui-Gon, Obi-Wan is more brooding and cautious than his teacher. He is careful to weigh the consequences of his actions and is reluctant to entangle himself unnecessarily in transgressions against the will of the Jedi High Council. A serious, quiet man possessed of a dry sense of humour, Obi-Wan strives to be worthy of his order and feels honoured to be Qui-Gon's student, although he worries about his Master's tendency to take risks in defiance of the Council. Nevertheless, Obi-Wan follows Qui-Gon Jinn's example and develops an independent spirit of his own.

UTILITY BELT

Belt fastener

Fastener band

Utility belt

Traditional leather

Food and tool pouches

BREATHER POUCH

## Jedi Gear

The basic Jedi clothing of belted tunic, travel boots and robe speaks of the simplicity vested in Jedi philosophy and carries overtones of their mission as travellers. Individual Jedi keep utility belt field gear to a minimum. As initiates are taught in the great Temple, Jedi reputations are based on their spirits and not on material trappings.

UTILITY POUCHES
On field missions, Jedi carry a basic kit consisting of food capsules, medical supplies, multitools and other essential devices.

FOOD AND ENERGY CAPSULES

Rugged travel boots

## A99 Aquata Breather

In this era, Jedi Knights usually carry various high-tech devices concealed in their robes or in belt pouches. On their mission to Naboo, Obi-Wan and Qui-Gon Jinn carry A99 Aquata breathers, knowing that much of the planet's surface is water. Breathers allow the Jedi to survive underwater for up to two hours. In other times, Jedi have avoided such technological devices in order to minimize their dependence on anything but their own resourcefulness.

Regulator

Hinges for storage

Mouthpiece

Compressed air tanks

Blade modulation circuitry

Blade emitter

Blade length and intensity control

Activator

Internal blade crystals

Single main internal power cell

Handgrip

Charging port

Power cell reserve cap

Faced with the mechanized minions of the Trade Federation droid army, Obi-Wan knows that he need not exercise the combat restraint he would use with living beings. He puts his fight training to good use, yet maintains cool concentration.

# Lightsabre

Lightsabres follow a common design. Optional elements, like blade power and length modulators, are small and unobtrusive. Accordingly, Jedi lightsabres appear similar at first glance. A closer inspection, however, reveals that lightsabres rarely look exactly alike. All are hand-built by the initiates themselves, making design details a matter of individual choice. Most Padawan apprentices build their lightsabres to resemble those of their teachers as a mark of respect.

Voice pickup

Encoder

Silencer

OBI-WAN KENOBI'S COMLINK

Centred awareness

Battle stance

Blue lightsabre blade

Hyperdrive diagnostic monitor

Warning mark indicates energy leak

Damaged priming pylons

Obi-Wan Kenobi views Anakin Skywalker as an unnecessary risk, both as a travel companion and as a potential Jedi. But at Qui-Gon Jinn's request, Obi-Wan accepts Anakin as his apprentice, beginning a long and fateful relationship.

# Hyperdrive

When the hyperdrive generator of the Naboo Royal Starship is damaged, Obi-Wan stays on board to look after the drive core while Qui-Gon seeks a replacement generator. Constantly monitoring the damaged component, Obi-Wan readies the core for repairs.

Obi-Wan is an exceptional lightsabre duelist and a formidable opponent for Darth Maul. The Sith Lord fights with inhuman intensity, fuelled by the hateful energy of the dark side of the Force. In the heat of mortal combat and on the brink of death, Obi-Wan faces the temptation to draw on the same terrible strength in order to defeat his enemy.

## DATA FILE

◆ Jedi robes are virtually indistinguishable from the simple robes worn by many species throughout the galaxy. This signifies the Jedi pledge to the service and protection of even the most humble galactic citizen.

◆ Obi-Wan remains loyal to Qui-Gon even when this puts him at odds with the Jedi High Council.

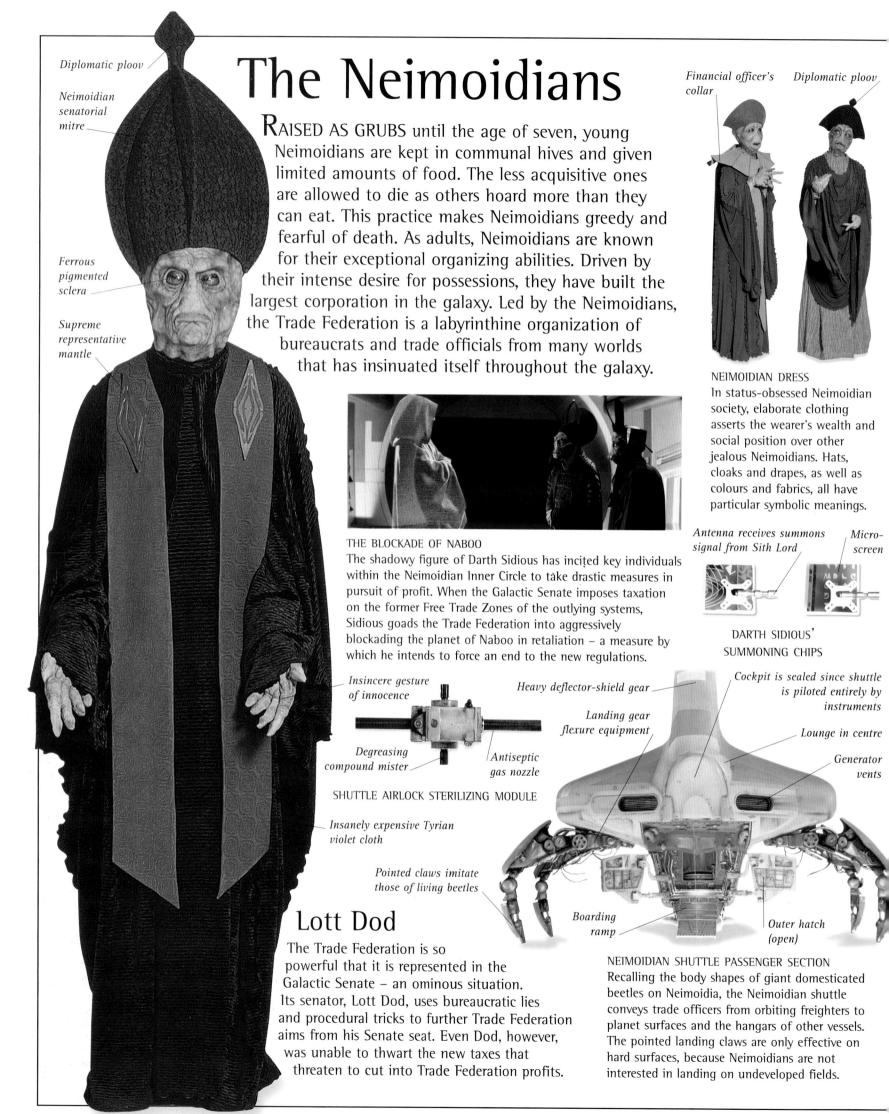

# The Neimoidians

RAISED AS GRUBS until the age of seven, young Neimoidians are kept in communal hives and given limited amounts of food. The less acquisitive ones are allowed to die as others hoard more than they can eat. This practice makes Neimoidians greedy and fearful of death. As adults, Neimoidians are known for their exceptional organizing abilities. Driven by their intense desire for possessions, they have built the largest corporation in the galaxy. Led by the Neimoidians, the Trade Federation is a labyrinthine organization of bureaucrats and trade officials from many worlds that has insinuated itself throughout the galaxy.

*Diplomatic ploov*

*Neimoidian senatorial mitre*

*Ferrous pigmented sclera*

*Supreme representative mantle*

*Financial officer's collar*

*Diplomatic ploov*

### NEIMOIDIAN DRESS
In status-obsessed Neimoidian society, elaborate clothing asserts the wearer's wealth and social position over other jealous Neimoidians. Hats, cloaks and drapes, as well as colours and fabrics, all have particular symbolic meanings.

### THE BLOCKADE OF NABOO
The shadowy figure of Darth Sidious has incited key individuals within the Neimoidian Inner Circle to take drastic measures in pursuit of profit. When the Galactic Senate imposes taxation on the former Free Trade Zones of the outlying systems, Sidious goads the Trade Federation into aggressively blockading the planet of Naboo in retaliation – a measure by which he intends to force an end to the new regulations.

*Antenna receives summons-signal from Sith Lord*

*Micro-screen*

### DARTH SIDIOUS' SUMMONING CHIPS

*Insincere gesture of innocence*

*Heavy deflector-shield gear*

*Landing gear flexure equipment*

*Cockpit is sealed since shuttle is piloted entirely by instruments*

*Lounge in centre*

*Generator vents*

*Degreasing compound mister*

*Antiseptic gas nozzle*

### SHUTTLE AIRLOCK STERILIZING MODULE

*Insanely expensive Tyrian violet cloth*

*Pointed claws imitate those of living beetles*

*Boarding ramp*

*Outer hatch (open)*

## Lott Dod

The Trade Federation is so powerful that it is represented in the Galactic Senate – an ominous situation. Its senator, Lott Dod, uses bureaucratic lies and procedural tricks to further Trade Federation aims from his Senate seat. Even Dod, however, was unable to thwart the new taxes that threaten to cut into Trade Federation profits.

### NEIMOIDIAN SHUTTLE PASSENGER SECTION
Recalling the body shapes of giant domesticated beetles on Neimoidia, the Neimoidian shuttle conveys trade officers from orbiting freighters to planet surfaces and the hangars of other vessels. The pointed landing claws are only effective on hard surfaces, because Neimoidians are not interested in landing on undeveloped fields.

# Rune Haako

As Settlement Officer of the Trade Federation armed forces, Rune Haako serves as diplomatic attaché and legal counsel to Nute Gunray. Haako has a reputation for ruthlessly treating business partners as adversaries and conniving to wrest every last credit from them.

Neimoidians are cautious by nature and the Trade Federation has always been careful to hide its acts of extortion and manipulation behind lies and protests of good faith. Their open aggression against Naboo is new territory for them, and both Gunray and Haako are uneasy about the possibility of escalation.

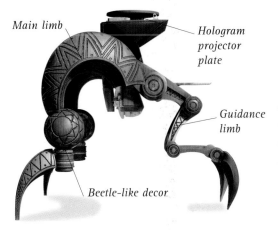

*Main limb*

*Hologram projector plate*

*Guidance limb*

*Beetle-like decor*

## MECHNO-CHAIR

Walking mechno-chairs are neither comfortable nor practical. However, they are hugely expensive and express the high status of their user. They also serve as platforms for hologram transmissions of high-ranking individuals.

# Nute Gunray

*Attorney's cowl*

A Commanding Viceroy of the Trade Federation, Nute Gunray wields great authority and serves on the Trade Federation Executive Board. Deceitful and willing to kill for his far-reaching commercial aims, Gunray directs the actions of the secret army fleet from the bridge of the flagship.

*Viceroy's crested tiara*

*Wheedling expression*

*Viceroy's collar*

*Underhanded gesture*

## DATA FILE

◆ The Neimoidians' organizational skills come from running mass hives and vast fungus farms on their home world of Neimoidia.

◆ Trade Federation freighters, hauling cargo between the far-flung stars of the Republic, are a familiar sight in orbit above many civilized worlds.

# The Invasion Force

WHEN ITS BLOCKADE fails to intimidate the Naboo Queen into submission, the Trade Federation prepares for the next step: invasion. The Sith Lord Darth Sidious persuades Neimoidian Viceroy Nute Gunray to order the deployment of an immense secret army hidden in the cargo hangars of converted trade freighters. The Naboo little suspect the magnitude of this force, and the Neimoidian leader commits the outrage in confidence that the weak politicians of the Galactic Senate will not object. In support of his evil plans, the viceroy is aided by the cowardly captain of the war fleet command vessel, Daultay Dofine, as well as droid soldiers and powerful war craft.

*Data goggles allow pilot to see constant holographic data read-outs*

*Vessel command officer's mitre*

*Skin mottled from self-indulgence*

*Comlink*

Daultay Dofine reports to Neimoidian Viceroy Nute Gunray.

## Daultay Dofine

Captain of the Trade Federation's flagship vessel, Daultay Dofine has climbed the ladder of rank through a combination of high birth, back-stabbing and grovelling behaviour towards his superiors. Nevertheless, Dofine finds the bold plans of the Sith Lord Darth Sidious too dangerous for his tastes. However, he soon learns that his tastes are entirely irrelevant.

*Officer's drape*

A fleet of specially-built C-9979 craft land the Trade Federation invasion force on Naboo. These landing craft are built to hold heavy armour and legions of troops in their bodies and repulsorlift wings. Groups of three landing craft are deployed in a pattern that cuts off all the Naboo cities from each other.

MTTs are dispatched to strategic positions, where they thunder along programmed routes.

*Droid deployment hatch*

*Heavy armour plating*

*Repulsorlift exhaust system*

### DATA FILE

◆ Wargame exercises and action against bandits threatening trade routes tested all aspects of the Trade Federation army, ensuring that the force is completely invincible ... or so it seems.

◆ The wealthy, arrogant Neimoidians tend to avoid any kind of labour, preferring to use droids instead.

Although Trade Federation war craft have only been used in exercises and skirmishes before their deployment on Naboo, their minimum-cost paint is already badly chipped. This attests to the Neimoidians' dedication to cheapness even in this profitable and long-awaited enterprise.

Protocol droid TC-14 ignores the foul play brewing against the Jedi ambassadors for the Supreme Chancellor. When the Jedi visitors are hit with poison gas, TC-14 simply wants to get out of the way, apologizing even to the battle droids outside the meeting room.

Underestimating the number of blaster turrets bristling from the Trade Federation war freighters, Naboo pilot Ric Olié takes a near-collision course in his effort to escape the deadly line of fire.

## TC-14

*Frequent memory erasures ensure docility*

*Neutral humanoid form*

Serving Viceroy Nute Gunray and his lieutenant Rune Haako of the Trade Federation, TC-14 acts as servant and translator during trade negotiations with foreign cultures. TC-14 is often employed to distract official guests while legal manipulation is carried out behind their backs.

*Hangar arm*  *Centresphere*  *War forces carried in interior*

*Armour-plated hull*

*Restraining bolt mount*

*Triple quadlaser batteries*

Trade Federation freighters seem harmless from a distance. Enemies are lulled into a false sense of security – until the heavy quadlaser batteries start firing.

## War Freighter

To carry the forces of its army, the Trade Federation has secretly converted its commercial freighter fleet into battleships, replete with shields, blaster turrets, and military communication arrays. These disguised war freighters hide the deadly battle machines until they are right on top of their enemies—or, as the Trade Federation prefers to call them, "future customers."

*Multi-system connection wires*

*Walking wing in attack mode*

SIDE VIEW

WALK MODE

*Active sensor 'eye'*

*Flight assault lasers*

*Walking limbtips*

*Droid Control Ship*

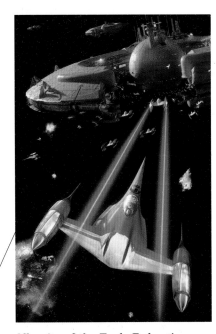

*Subservient posture*

*Polished silver finish*

*Reinforced knee joint*

*Shinplate*

*Foot shell*

## Droid Starfighter

The complex, precision-engineered droid starfighters built for the Trade Federation by the Xi Char cathedral factories are variable-geometry machines. The long, wing-like claws open to reveal deadly laser cannons. On the ground, these "wings" become movable legs as the fighter shifts to walk mode for surface patrol.

All units of the Trade Federation droid army are controlled by the Central Control Computer on board a modified war freighter. Without the control signal, droids shut down, making the Droid Control Ship a key target whose destruction could wipe out the entire invasion force.

# Battle Droids

THE GALACTIC REPUBLIC has survived disagreements, standoffs and even rebellion among its many member worlds, relying on the Jedi Knights to quell conflicts. In this enlightened age, few standing armies are maintained that serve anything other than ceremonial purposes, since an army could be regarded as an open threat to galactic peace. Nevertheless, as the bureaucracy of the Republic Senate indulges in endless debates and procedural bickering, the use of force has become a real threat. The wealthy Trade Federation has quietly gone far beyond any other group in assembling a massive army composed of ghostly, emotionless droid soldiers that are ready to do their masters' bidding without a touch of emotion or mercy. Their deployment upon the peaceful people of Naboo heralds the end of an age of peace and security in the galaxy.

Sensory input cable

Receiver assembly casing

Magnetic stabilizing field bar

Signal clarifier septode

Signal confirmation module

Speech transmission lines

Interference dissipator mat

Stored vocabulary triggered by control impulses

Vocoder

Signal reception boost antenna

Specialized movement processor

Signal transmission lines

Dephasing anticode sieve

Code processing baffles

Signal receiver assembly

Sampled movement cycle memory

Signal boost and power augment backpack

Override signal receptor

Speech processor

Transmitter boost antenna

General command storage

Optical sensor

Arm extension piston

High-torque motors

## Battle Droid Head

The battle droid head, lacking a brain of its own, contains little more than a large and sensitive control signal receiver. Small processors collect movement and limited sensory data for transmission back to the Central Control Computer, and a vocoder enables the droid to talk.

STAP
Battle droid scouts and antipersonnel clean-up snipers are swept through the air on an armed Single Trooper Aerial Platforms. The repulsorlift minimal structure allows it to thread its way through dense forest that would be inaccessible to larger vehicles. The droid pilot rides exposed to enemy fire.

STAP's

## Command Officer

In order to streamline communication between Trade Federation officials and droid troops, certain battle droids, such as OOM-9, are designated Command Officers. Orders are conveyed to officer droids via priority channels from the Central Control Computer processors.

*Droid type designation markings*

*Enemy mass reading*

*Macrobinoculars*

*Enemy charge reading*

*Stereo image rangefinder*

OFFICER'S MACROBINOCULARS

OOM-9

Command Officer

Security droid

Pilot droid

Infantry battle droid

### DROID TYPES

Battle droids are structurally identical irrespective of job function. To increase efficiency, however, droids are pre-programmed with specialized subroutines. Infantry and Command Officer droids are fitted with power backpacks to boost operational range and extend recharge intervals.

*Dried cartilage-shaped shin plates*

ПヨϽ∩ϽΙϾϽϤ
1 2 3 4 5 6 7 8 9

GALACTIC BASIC NUMERALS
IDENTIFY INDIVIDUAL DROIDS

### DATA FILE

◆ Their lack of independent thought processors make battle droids immune to fear, cowardice or mercy pleas.

◆ The smooth movements of battle droids are the result of pre-digitized motion-capture data taken from live soldiers and broadcast by the Central Control Computer to each droid.

*Legs fully upright*

*Generic feet can be replaced with claws or pads*

## Battle Droid Blaster

*Waste energy conduit*

*Blaster gas cartridge*

*Power cell*

*Continuous-fire trigger*

*Entire barrel can be replaced with broad-fire pattern tip*

Since battle droids are capable of wielding deadly blasters, they are designed to be incapable of independent thought. They are governed entirely by the Central Control Computer and have no ability to react to surprises or learn from experience. While battle droids can be deadly, their firing accuracy is poor.

*Head is deployed last*

*Legs unfold*

*Arms unbend*

*Claws grip legs for stability*

*Blaster stored on backpack while droid is compressed*

### UNFOLDING DROID

For efficient storage, battle droids are built to fold up tightly, compressing to minimal volume. In compressed configuration, 112 droids can be carried in the special deployment rack of an MTT.

*Skull husk head*

*Imitation brain sac*

*Bonelike arm*

Battle droids are designed to resemble skeletal Neimoidian bodies in order to look threatening. When left unburied and unburned, Neimoidian brain mantles wither to dried sacs behind the top of the skull and their noseless faces stretch and warp to a characteristic shape. This vile image of death defines the droid's features.

# Droidekas

To MAKE UP for the weaknesses of battle droids, a special contract was awarded for the creation of an altogether different combat droid that would be a much more serious weapon. The design was created by a species of chitinous Colicoids in their own image on a planet far from the Republic's core. Colicoids are known for their completely unfeeling and murderous ways, and Colla IV has been embroiled for many years in diplomatic disputes related to the death and consumption of visitors to the system. The droideka was exactly what concerned Trade Federation officers wanted: a formidable, heavy-duty killing machine to back up the battle droids in the face of determined opposition.

Using a combination of momentum and repulsor effects, droidekas unfurl in a matter of seconds from wheel form into standing position, ready to attack.

The dramatic transformation recalls the attack pattern of a deadly adult Colicoid, and can take unwary opponents by surprise – as the droids' manufacturers intended.

*Triad active sensor antennas*

**FRONT VIEW**

Head-on to an attacker, a droideka presents blazing guns and a fearsome image as well as a minimal target silhouette for opponents who survive long enough to return fire.

*Reactor cooling vanes*

*Case-hardened bronzium armour shell*

**BACK VIEW**

Desperate enemies attempting to attack a droideka from behind find that its armour is extremely effective, and its moving legs and gun arms are hard to hit.

*Backshell plate protects weapons while droideka is rolling toward enemy*

*Lateral boom for weapon arm*

*Primary rolling surface*

*Sensor head*

*Sensor antenna*

*Sternum plate*

*Folded forward leg*

*Heavy plate upper weapon arm*

*Pointed claw foot*

*Rear leg*

*Deflector shield projector flaps*

## Wheel Form

For compact storage and optimum travel speed, droidekas retract into the shape of a wheel. Using pulsed internal micro-repulsors in sequence, they roll themselves into battle, opening at the last minute into their combat form. In transit, the wheel configuration presents a smaller and faster target to enemy gunfire.

Qui-Gon Jinn and Obi-Wan Kenobi evade or cut down battle droids with relative ease. But when destroyer droids attack, the Jedi cannot hold them off indefinitely and Qui-Gon knows they must escape.

Droidekas carry their own deflector shield generators that can completely repel pistol fire and substantially weaken high-energy rifle or artillery bolts. This makes them devastating and nearly invincible in combat.

Collimating tip concentrates blaster bolt energy

Arm extensor strut

Blaster energizer

Blaster power cable

Non-visual composite radiation sensor antennas

Fine vibration sensor

Primary sensor antenna

Blaster power converter

Sensor head

Pneumatic limb charger

Sternum plate

Spinal power cell series

Power cell plating

Deflector shield projector plate

Blaster heat dissipator cowl

Backshell plate

Pneumatic pressure conduit

Power cable

Twin high-energy blaster

Shield plates open in combat stance

Hip joint

Mini-reactor bulb

Case-hardened bronzium armour bulb protects reactor

Repulsor lifts droid

Legs guide droid

Foot claw designed for hard surfaces

## Combat Stance

When a droideka is ready to begin an assault, it quickly unfolds and stands up on three legs. Its pneumatic arms flex open and its eerie head rises with its enemy-finding sensors ablaze. Made only for combat and specialized for the single purpose of destruction, the droideka has no need of hands. Instead, powerful twin blasters are built onto its arms. Unlike the lightly built battle droids, every part of the droideka is heavy alloy or armour plate, making the machine a fearsome spectre that cuts down soldiers by the dozen with ease.

Droidekas generate shields using on-board mini-reactors contained in their armoured bases. These reactors also power the droids' volt-guzzling movement systems and high-energy blasters.

### DATA FILE

◆ Like battle droids, droidekas have no independent logic processors and are run by the Central Control Computer signal. The Colicoids dislike this system and have built custom droidekas equipped with computer brains.

◆ Droidekas are commonly known as destroyer droids in many parts of the galaxy.

# Queen Amidala

AMIDALA rules as Queen of the Naboo people at the age of only 14. She was raised by humble parents in a small mountain village, where her exceptional abilities were recognized early in life. Given the best training and pushed to develop her capabilities, she became Princess of Theed, the Naboo capital city, at the age of 12. Amidala was elected Queen upon the abdication of the previous sovereign, Veruna, who had become embroiled in outworld politics after a rule of 13 years. The Naboo trusted that Amidala would hold their interests close to her heart—but had no idea of the crisis looming ahead.

Beaded emblems over 240 years old, taken from an earlier queen's gown

Foreknot

Large oversleeves

Suspensas

Painted thumbnail

Black Cyrene silk fabric

Feet hidden for stateliness

**FOREIGN RESIDENCE GOWN**
On Coruscant, Amidala wears a dark gown befitting the gravity of her situation. This subdued foreign residence gown acknowledges Amidala's separation from Naboo and the peril her people face.

Jewel of Zenda

Gold faceframes

Hair combed over a padded form

Wide shoulders make Amidala seem larger

Hand-stitched gold embroidery

White thumbnail polish is the only tradition Amidala retains from her native village

## Throne-Room Gown

Amidala draws upon Naboo's deeply traditional modes of royal dress and make-up to express the commitment she has to her role. Her extremely formal appearance in the palace throne room helps her project an unwaveringly professional image and warns others not to dismiss her abilities.

Shed potolli fur cuffs

Illuminated sein jewel

Wide gown flare hides feet

Amidala sits in state in Theed Palace, hearing cases and reports from the Advisory Council. With her clear perception, she inspires confidence even in seasoned and hard-edged men like Captain Panaka.

Antique tiara

Mauve chersilk hair veil

Full cerlin sleeves

Drapa bindings

Multilayered gown

**AMIDALA'S TRAVELLING GOWN**

When Queen Amidala travels aboard the Naboo Royal Starship, she holds court in a spacious throne room. Amidala uses a holoprojector to communicate with Governor Sio Bibble back on Naboo.

The Queen's gowns are set off with many fine details, such as beads and suspensa ornaments. Many of these come from the palace treasure rooms.

**GOLD BEADS**

Amidala's stylized white make-up draws upon Naboo's ancient royal customs. The red 'scar of remembrance' marks Naboo's time of suffering, before the Great Time of Peace.

*Scar of remembrance divides lip*

*Stylized beauty marks display symmetry*

**NABOO VICTORY PARADE**

*Escoffiate headpiece*

*Royal Sovereign of Naboo medal*

*Golden hairbands*

*Suspensas made of delicate orichalc finework*

*Royal diadem*

*Minimal jewellery for simplicity*

*Jewelled finials*

*Aurate fan in ancient Naboo royal fashion, signifying continuity*

## Senate Gown

When Amidala pleads for her people before the Galactic Senate, she appears in an extraordinary gown and hairstyle that express the majesty of the free people of Naboo. The regal attire also hides Amidala's feelings and helps her stay courageous and aloof.

*Grand finial hairtip ornaments balance escoffiate headpiece*

*Golden, triple-braided soutache*

*Embossed rosette*

*Petalled cape*

*Plain white gown expresses the pure happiness of newfound peace*

## Parade Gown

After the victory over the Trade Federation, Amidala appears in a parade gown markedly different from her robes of office. The silken petals of the dress resemble huge, lovely flowers found near Amidala's home village. These flowers bloom only once every 88 years, heralding a time of special celebration.

### DATA FILE

◆ Naboo's monarchy is not hereditary: rulers are elected by their people on merit. Queen Amidala is not the youngest sovereign ever to rule.

◆ Amidala can step down from the throne whenever she chooses.

# The Queen's Handmaidens

DEDICATED AND LOW-KEY, the royal handmaidens shadow Queen Amidala at all times. This select group maintains Amidala's regal image, assisting behind the scenes with her elaborate gowns, hairstyles and make-up. They also quietly protect Amidala, acting as secret bodyguards. Upon Amidala's coronation, the handmaidens were hand-picked for their intelligence, courage, fitness and resemblance to Amidala. Although the Queen has known them for just half a year, she values their company. In particular, she has become close friends with the dependable and cool-headed Sabé.

## Rabé

In spite of her young age, Rabé has learned to exercise great patience in her role as handmaiden to the Queen. She soothes Amidala's nerves and helps to prepare her exotic hairstyles, which can require several hours to perfect.

*Oversleeves in the Naboo style*

*Soft trevella cloth*

*Gown tinted with spectra-fade dye*

*Feather headdress*

*Gemstone and filigree ear covering*

*Hood to hide face*

*Amidala disguised as a hand-maiden*

## Sabé

The most important handmaiden is Sabé. First in line to become the royal decoy in times of danger, she dresses as the Queen and hides her features with white make-up. Amidala has coached Sabé in regal bearing and speech. Even so, she plays the role with apprehension, concerned that a subtle slip will give her sovereign away.

*Luggage container*      *Wardrobe container*

TRAVELLING IN STYLE
The Royal Starship is equipped with wardrobe containers. From these containers, the handmaidens choose an elaborate dress for the Queen's appearance before the Senate.

*Micrograv activates when container is closed*

*Accessory holders*      *Climate-controlled interior*

Disguised as Queen Amidala, Sabé is flanked by handmaidens in the throne room of the Royal Starship. The still, expressionless presence of the handmaidens lends dignity to the decoy Queen as she holds court.

## Travel luggage

The special wardrobe containers holding the Queen's wardrobe and jewellery include micrograv devices in their bases. These mechanisms ensure that clothes hang properly even if the closed container is tipped on its side.

## Battle Dress

In her guise as the Queen, Sabé wears a distinctive battle dress that allows her maximum freedom of movement. In the palace throne room, Sabe's disguise fools the Neimoidian viceroy and allows Amidala to reach a hidden pistol.

*Broad waistband*

*Surcoat*

*Long skirt made of blast-damping fabric*

*Medium-range barrel*

*Snap-action trigger*

*Power cell in grip*

*Shiraya fan headdress worn only by Queen Amidala*

ROYAL PISTOL
After being selected, the handmaidens were given bodyguard training. Each is capable of using a pistol to help defend the Queen in the unlikely event of a disturbance or emergency.

## Eirtaé

Handmaiden Eirtaé comes from a town in a remote river valley. Her family was wealthy and she was taught the demands of etiquette. She helps the other handmaidens – and sometimes the Queen – with royal protocol.

*Wide cowl masks Eirtaé's face*

*Gown decorated with the royal insignia*

*Veda pearl beading*

*Glass filaments*

*Rabé's simple gown sets off the majesty of the Queen's appearance*

*Sabé (disguised as Amidala)*

*Eirtaé*

*Rabé*

*Saché*

*Yané*

IN ATTENDANCE
Just as Amidala wears a particular dress for each different official occasion, the handmaidens dress in matching, complementary clothes.

### DATA FILE

◆ Amidala has five handmaidens: Rabé, Eirtaé, Sabé, Saché and Yané.

◆ Rabé, Eirtaé and Sabé accompany the Queen when she escapes Theed on the Royal Starship, while Saché and Yané reluctantly stay behind.

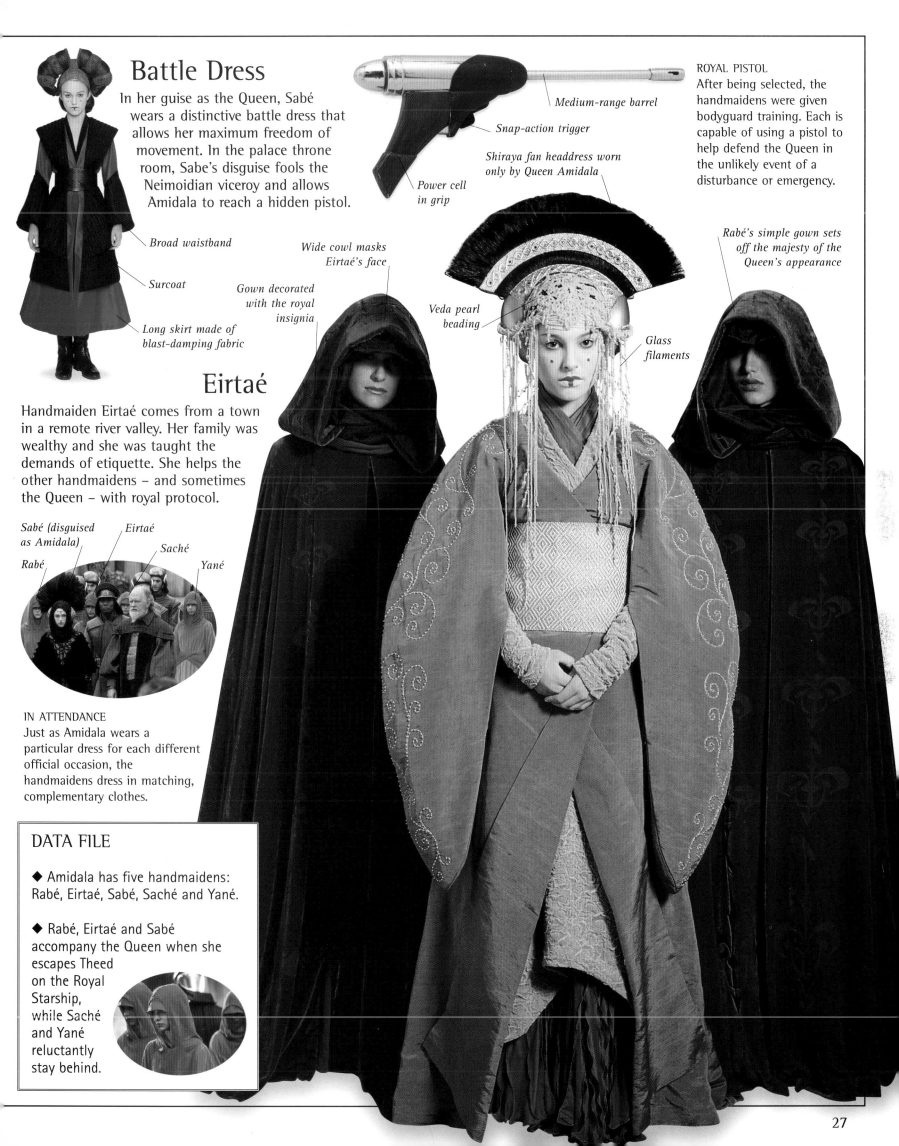

27

# Padmé Naberrie

WHENEVER THE QUEEN is exposed to danger, she disguises herself as one of her own handmaidens, taking the name Padmé Naberrie. The identical hooded dresses and similar appearance of Amidala's handmaidens make it easy for Padmé to appear and disappear quietly from the group. When Padmé is among the attendants, handmaiden Sabé impersonates the Queen, subtly taking signals from Padmé regarding royal decisions. Captain Panaka is behind the creation of Amidala's double identity, having explained the old Palace scheme to her upon her coronation. In her guise as Padmé, Amidala accompanies Qui-Gon Jinn to Mos Espa to see for herself what the Jedi is up to.

Simple braids

Rough-spun cloth

Glass jewel of little value

In Mos Espa, the disguised Queen finds Qui-Gon Jinn's risky plans not to her liking but she cannot use her regal authority to object. Nonetheless, she realizes that the Jedi Master has the benefit of long experience, and she goes along with his scheme while harbouring her doubts.

Amidala's disguise fools nearly everyone, but nine-year-old Anakin Skywalker quickly sees that Padmé is special. He is drawn to her, and she returns his affection, not quite knowing what to make of the gifted young boy.

## Peasant Dress

When Qui-Gon Jinn determines to go into Mos Espa, Padmé decides to keep an eye on him. Captain Panaka, the Naboo Head of Security, promises to look after the ship. Rough peasant clothing helps Padmé blend in as an anonymous farm girl.

Removing her white facepaint is a key element in the success of Amidala's disguise as Padmé. People are so accustomed to the Queen's formal royal appearance that they do not give ordinary-looking Padmé a second glance.

Traditional Tatooine sand symbols

Japor ivory wood snippet obtained by Anakin through trading

Jerba leather cord

LUCKY CHARM
Knowing that the future is uncertain, especially his own, Anakin carves a good-luck charm for Padmé. He hopes that she will remember him by this token in spite of what may happen to each of them.

Wrist bindings keep out sand and dust

Plain walking boots

### DATA FILE

◆ Padmé and Sabé practice indirect communication in private, making a game of speaking in cryptic ways. This practice makes it easier for Padmé to guide Sabé's actions as Queen.

◆ As humble Padmé, Amidala observes things that might not be revealed to the Queen.

Being disguised as Padmé robs Amidala of her regal power but gives her the freedom to live as a normal person. In Mos Espa, she assists with Anakin's Podracer and helps out where needed.

## Padmé in Battle

Padmé judges that by capturing the Neimoidian leaders she can end the invasion and bring her enemies to justice for their crimes. Her determined presence among her own troops inspires them to success against the odds. Sabé remains disguised as the Queen to the end, providing Padmé with a critical advantage at the last minute.

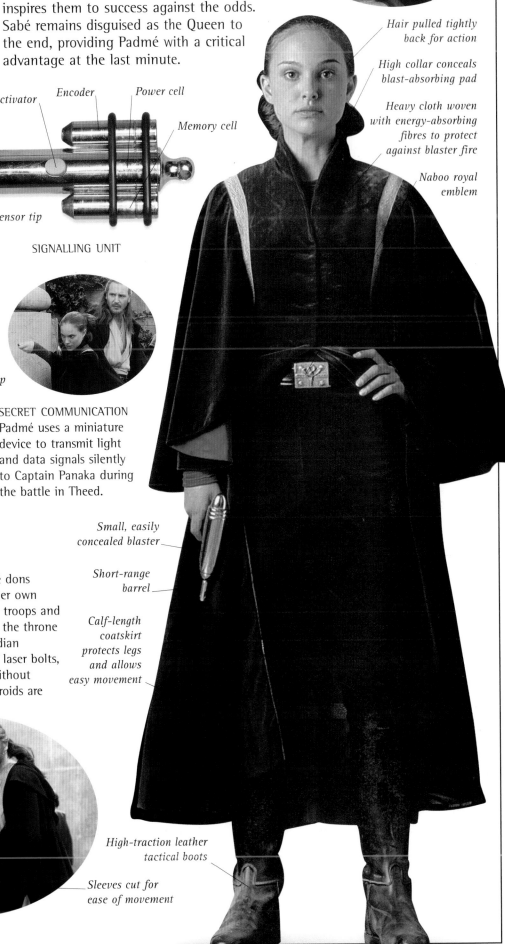

*Hair pulled tightly back for action*

*High collar conceals blast-absorbing pad*

*Heavy cloth woven with energy-absorbing fibres to protect against blaster fire*

*Naboo royal emblem*

**MESSAGE FROM NABOO**
While travelling to Coruscant, Padmé is tortured by the replay of Sio Bibble's hologram transmission, which tells of catastrophic death back on Naboo. Is it a trap? The truth? Or both? It takes great resolve for Padmé to stick to her plan of pleading Naboo's cause in the Galactic Senate when what she most wants is to be with her suffering people.

*Activator*   *Encoder*   *Power cell*

*Memory cell*

*Emitter/sensor tip*

SIGNALLING UNIT

*Minimal barrel makes blaster easy to hide*

*Smooth shell design allows blaster to be slipped out from concealment easily*

*Blaster gas cartridge cap*

*Snap trigger requires firm squeeze to prevent misfires*

*Energy cell in handgrip*

## Blaster

Padmé and the other handmaidens carry versions of the slim royal pistol. It is designed for practical use and easy concealment. The streamlined blasters pack a mild punch compared to true security guns, but they fire plasma bolts that can be deadly.

**SECRET COMMUNICATION**
Padmé uses a miniature device to transmit light and data signals silently to Captain Panaka during the battle in Theed.

*Small, easily concealed blaster*

*Short-range barrel*

*Calf-length coatskirt protects legs and allows easy movement*

**RETURN TO THE PALACE**
On her return to Naboo, Padmé dons battle dress. In the assault on her own palace, she fights alongside her troops and the Jedi allies in order to reach the throne room and confront the Neimoidian invaders. Braving onslaughts of laser bolts, Padmé is quick to return fire without qualms: she knows the battle droids are not living foes.

In Naboo's most desperate hour, Padmé reveals her secret identity to the Gungan ruler, Boss Nass. She knows that only a clear token of good faith such as this could win over the stubborn Gungan.

*High-traction leather tactical boots*

*Sleeves cut for ease of movement*

# The Naboo

THE PEOPLE OF NABOO have prospered under the security of the Republic, advancing their society without concern for outside threats. Naboo is governed by an elected sovereign, a Governor and an Advisory Council residing in the Royal Palace at the capital city of Theed. The Naboo live in cities and villages that are thinly scattered on the main landmass of their planet. A love of art is deeply seated in Naboo culture, taking such forms as grand architecture and elaborate clothing fashions. The Naboo regard their refined way of life as a birthright, but they will find that it is a luxury that they will have to defend.

**NABOO**
The planet Naboo is small, green and honeycombed by a curious crustal substructure that is riddled with cave passages.

*Formal collar*

*Fashionable Naboo sleeves and cuffs*

**THEED**
The crown jewel of Naboo civilization is the city of Theed, built at the edge of a great plateau where the River Solleu winds its way towards a spectacular waterfall. Artisans, architects and urban planners are all valued highly in Naboo culture, and their splendid city is a special testament to their efforts.

## Sio Bibble

As governor of Naboo, the outspoken Sio Bibble oversees all matters brought to the Queen's attention. He also chairs the Advisory Council, and deals directly with regional representatives and town governing officials in day-to-day administration.

**CULTURAL CAPITAL**
In addition to the Royal Palace, the greatest Naboo libraries, museums, shrines, theatres, and conservatories are located in Theed. The city's buildings are designed in the classical Naboo style.

*Domed roofs common on Naboo's buildings*

*Zoorif feather motif*　　NABOO JEWELLERY　　*Organic chif stone*

Sio Bibble is loath to concede to Captain Panaka's dire warnings of greater need for armament. A noble philosopher, he even refuses to change his mind during his planet's most desperate hour.

*Philosopher's tunic*

**THE ADVISORY COUNCIL**
The members of the Royal Advisory Council present matters to the Queen and offer her their expertise. The Council frequently changes the composition of its membership bringing a range of scholars, artists and interested community members into the Queen's audience.

*Governor's boots*

*Formal hairstyle*

*Robe of state*

**HELA BRANDES**
MUSIC ADVISOR

**GRAF ZAPALO**
MASTER OF SCIENCES

**HUGO ECKENER**
CHIEF ARCHITECT

**LUFTA SHIF**
EDUCATION ADVISOR

# Royal Starship

The gleaming Naboo Royal Starship conveys Queen Amidala to formal state appearances in matchless style. Built on Naboo using foreign-made engine and technology components, the ship blends the Naboo love of art with the industrial power available from other worlds.

**ROYAL PERFECTION**
The Royal Starship is quite unlike craft from other planets. Its distinctive interior is characterized by elegant curves and a clean, refined look. As with much Naboo design, utility is secondary to aesthetic concerns.

*Hand-finished chromium finish is a royal prerogative*

*Starship carries no weapons*

*Throne room*

*Sublight engine*

*Heat sink finial makes fuel burn cleaner*

*High-resolution eyepiece*

*Talo-effect "lens" allows subatomic analysis*

**DAMAGE MONITOR**
The Royal Starship has elaborate built-in systems to monitor equipment. When the ship suffers laser hits from the Trade Federation blockade, pilot Ric Olié can see at a glance exactly what has been damaged.

*Enlarged section showing damage*

*View mode indicator allows different internal representations*

*Starship overview*

*Power cells pulse energy through equipment to be tested*

*Diagnostic block*

**HIGH-END INSTRUMENTS**
High-precision diagnostic and analysis instruments on board the Royal Starship allow the crew to conduct a variety of tests. The wide range of instruments is capable of anticipating problems before they occur.

MESON TALOSCOPE

*Touch control*

ENGINEERING ANALYSIS BOARD

## DATA FILE

◆ Merchants on the fringes of Naboo's cities carry on a vital trade between their society and that of the Gungans.

◆ On board the Royal Starship, even simple components like this oscillation overthemister are handcrafted in the elegant Naboo style.

**FORMAL FUTHARK**
The Naboo alphabet has a traditional handwritten form, the futhork, and a formal form, called the futhark. The formal script, based on ovals, is used for purposes such as spacecraft identifications and control labels.

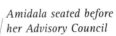

**SOCIAL FABRIC**
Clothing is often used as a form of social communication. During the Trade Federation blockade, citizens of Theed make subtle use of Naboo colour and fashion symbolism to express their support or opposition to the Queen's policies.

*Columns made of polished Naboo stone*

*Large windows lend serenity*

*Amidala seated before her Advisory Council*

# Theed Palace

Built centuries ago, the Royal Palace is the largest building in Theed. Its courts are used for meetings, dinners, parties, cultural events and visiting dignitaries. The palace blends historic design facets with automatic doors, communications systems and area-specific climate control.

*Palace Guard*

*Composite holoprojector built into floor*

Gestures of reassurance in the streets of Theed mask underlying tensions as people begin to grow hungry from the blockade. Some wonder whether their Queen will abandon them for her own safety.

31

# Captain Panaka

As Head of Security for Queen Amidala, Captain Panaka oversees every branch of the volunteer Royal Naboo Security Forces and is personally responsible for the Queen's safety. Panaka was appointed after his predecessor, Captain Magneta, failed to prevent the death of the former King Veruna, who had gone into hiding upon his abdication. Veruna's 'accidental' death was covered up – even from the Queen – and Magneta quietly resigned. Panaka sees the increasingly dangerous state of affairs in the galaxy and argues for stronger security measures to protect the Queen and Naboo itself. Despite this, the Advisory Council convinces Amidala to act in accordance with Naboo's traditional pacifism. Panaka foresees the outcome of this noble policy, but it takes the terror of an invasion to bring his point home.

*High officer headgear*

*Naboo Security crest*

*Leather jerkin covers thin anti-blast armour plates*

*Comlink in holster*

Panaka has the confidence of an experienced man and relies on his own judgment even when Jedi Knights step in. He believes that Qui-Gon Jinn's actions risk the Queen's safety and the fate of Naboo.

*Comlink attachment*

*Sturdy casing*

*Belt clip bracket*

**COMLINK HOLDER**

Panaka's security forces use small ground craft like the Gian landspeeder for patrols and general operations. These light speeders are some of the few assets Panaka has in his effort to retake Theed Palace from the invading droids.

## Blaster

*Rangefinding scope*

*Grappling hook (far side)*

*Primary sighting scope*

*Blaster gas cell chamber*

*Heat radiator ridges*

*Dart launcher*

*Gas-charged dart magazine*

*Heavy gripstock for firm control*

*Tip expands on impact to provide firm anchorage*

**GRAPPLING HOOK**

*Voice pickup*

*Transmitter*

*Handgrip*

**COMLINK**
Captain Panaka uses a master security comlink to keep in touch with his volunteer divisions, employing separate channels for command clarity.

The Royal Palace Guard use multi-function Security S-5 blaster guns. Not only do these weapons fire deadly blaster bolts, harmless sting charges, and anaesthetic microdarts, the S-5 blaster even includes a liquid-cable shooter that can coil around an enemy or let soldiers scale walls via a grappling-hook tip.

### DATA FILE

◆ Captain Panaka gained combat experience in a Republic Special Task Force fighting against space pirates in the sector containing the Naboo system.

◆ The Naboo Royal Security Forces include the Security Guard, the Palace Guard and the Space Fighter Corps. Local police answer to civilian authorities, not to Panaka.

# Security Officer

Panaka's few top officers are loyal but mostly unfamiliar with real danger. During the Trade Federation invasion, they work hard to maintain order in Naboo.

# Security Guard

Marshalled under the authority of Captain Panaka, the Security Guard is the closest thing to a regular infantry on Naboo. Individual Security Guards serve primarily as sentries and patrolmen in Theed, supplementing the Theed police force on behalf of the Royal Palace. Although well-drilled by Panaka, the Security Guard is no match for the mechanized army of the Trade Federation's invasion force.

Facing the Trade Federation forces, Panaka and his Palace Guard fight with determined efficiency to return the Queen to the throne.

# Palace Guard

The Palace Guard is the highly-trained bodyguard of the Queen and court. While the Security Guard function as a militia, the Palace Guard is made up of dedicated soldiers who typically experience battle off-planet and return to protect the Queen out of loyalty. Although few in number, the Palace Guard is the backbone of Naboo security.

*Officer's pistol*

*Officer's headgear*

*Wrist guard*

*Naboo Security crest*

*Combat helmet*

*Chin strap*

*Liquid cable shooter*

*Unarmoured joints for agility*

*Utility belt*

*Leather jerkin*

*CR-2 basic blaster, built to last*

*Resilient armour plates*

*Utility belt*

*Blast-damping armour*

*No leg armour*

*Traditional full cut thigh*

*Studded forearm plate for hand-to-hand combat*

*Shin protectors buckle over short boots*

*Auxiliary gear straps*

*High-traction, quiet-soled security boots*

*Uniform colour denotes Security Guard*

# Naboo Pilots

LIKE THEIR COMRADES the Security Guard and the Palace Guard, the Space Fighter Corps is a unit of the Royal Naboo Security Forces. Its pilots are a devil-may-care lot from diverse backgrounds who fly the custom-built Naboo N-1 Starfighters with pride. Their usual missions are routine patrols, escort duties or parade flights. Lack of combat on peaceful Naboo forces the pilots to gain experience off-planet in Republic pirate fighter groups or on the rare patrol missions that encounter troublemakers. By no means the most dangerous bunch of space pilots in the galaxy, the Space Fighter Corps are nonetheless ready for action – even in the face of the Trade Federation's overwhelming challenge.

Flying goggles

Anti-glare brim

Built-in communicator system

Flying jacket

Space Fighter Corps overcoat

Pilot safety harness attaches to ship's seat

Bright colours typical of Naboo style

Flying gloves

Naboo pilot-issue boots

## N-1 Starfighter

Partly finished in gleaming chromium to indicate royal status, N-1 starfighters sport radial engines of Nubian make in a J-configuration spaceframe. Assisted by an astromech droid, starfighters are fast and agile, but prone to uncontrollable spins when the engines suffer damage.

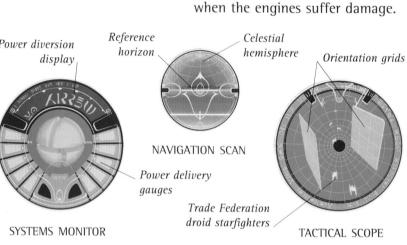

Power diversion display

Reference horizon

Celestial hemisphere

Orientation grids

Power delivery gauges

Trade Federation droid starfighters

SYSTEMS MONITOR

NAVIGATION SCAN

TACTICAL SCOPE

N-1 STARFIGHTER READ-OUTS
Starfighter pilots constantly monitor navigation and systems information from read-out panels arrayed in the cockpit.

Welded joints of armour shell

Automatic distress beacon

FLYING HELMET

## Ric Olié

The top pilot in the Space Fighter Corps is Ric Olié, a veteran flier who answers directly to Captain Panaka. Perfectly capable of flying any craft on Naboo, it is Ric Olié's honour to captain the Queen's Royal Starship. The run through the Neimoidian blockade taxes Olié's flying abilities to the limit, and even he doubts whether they can get through alive.

## DATA FILE

◆ Naboo pilots must gain experience flying utility craft before they are permitted to take the controls of a coveted N-1 starfighter.

◆ Only a few lucky pilots have ever flown royal escort duty all the way to Coruscant, most never having left Naboo's sector.

# R2-D2

**DROID HOLD**
In a small chamber on the lowest deck of the Naboo Royal Starship, R2-D2 recharges between work projects and waits with other astromech droids for assignments. A repulsorlift tube at one end of the hold conveys the droids to the outside of the ship for work on the hull during flight.

A UTILITY DROID with a mind of his own, there is more to R2-D2 than his ordinary appearance would suggest. Just one of several repair and maintenance droids assigned to the Naboo Royal Starship, R2-D2 replaces blown fuses, installs new wiring, polishes floors, and does whatever else is necessary to maintain the gleaming vessel in perfect working condition. For a utility droid, R2-D2 is equipped with remarkable tenacity and drive to accomplish his missions. Such dedication would ordinarily go unnoticed, but when crisis envelops the Royal Starship, R2-D2 becomes a hero.

*Astromech droid repair-monitor image*

*R2-D2 at work on the hull*

*Damaged deflector shield generator*

**IN-FLIGHT REPAIRS**
Astromech droids commonly carry out a wide variety of mechanical repair and information retrieval tasks. R2-D2 does not stand out from the crowd until he singlehandedly completes repairs to the Naboo Royal Starship's shield generator.

**COPILOT**
Standard astromech droids are used in many space fighters as on-board flight support. R2-D2 accompanies Anakin Skywalker into battle in the droid socket of a Naboo N-1 Starfighter.

*Secondary holographic projector*

*Primary photoreceptor and radar eye*

*Luminescent diagnostic display*

*Hydraulic arm shaft*

*Heat exhaust*

*Hydraulic extension arm*

*Optional oxidizer intake*

*Pneumatic cleaner*

*Sonic welder*

**REPAIR ARM**
This extendible arm can clean, cut or seal electronic components.

**ROCKET THRUSTER**
Accessory rocket thrusters give R2 units the ability to propel themselves through air or space.

*Thrust nozzle*

*Deployment brace*

*Control impulse and power net linkage*

*Inference pulse stabilizers*

*Sand-proof joints*

*Extendible third leg*

*Swivel-mounted tread*

*All-terrain main drive tread*

*Powerbus cables*

## DATA FILE

◆ R2-D2 is owned by the Royal House of Naboo. He was assigned to the Queen's ship because of his outstanding performance record.

◆ Artoo's head can telescope up so that he can see out of the tight neck of a Naboo Starfighter droid socket.

# Jar Jar Binks

AN AMPHIBIOUS GUNGAN native to Naboo, Jar Jar is a luckless exile from his home city, Otoh Gunga. He now lives in the swamps, where he survives on his own, eating raw shellfish and other such swamp fare. His long muscular tongue helps him to scoop molluscs out of their shells and tasty gumbols out of their tree burrows. During the invasion of Naboo, Qui-Gon Jinn runs into and rescues Jar Jar. The simple Gungan's sense of honour binds him to Qui-Gon for life, even though the Jedi would much rather do without him at first.

At first, Obi-Wan Kenobi dismisses Jar Jar as an inconvenient life form to have around. However, the Gungan quickly proves useful by telling the Jedi of an underwater city where they can escape from the ground forces of the Trade Federation.

## Gungan Survivor

Like all Gungans, Jar Jar's skeleton is made of cartilage, making him flexible and rubbery. Even his skull and jaws are elastic, giving the simple Gungan a wide range of facial expressions. Jar Jar's character, like his body, is resilient and able to bend to changes of fortune without letting his spirit break. Whether alone, in the company of Jedi or even among royalty, Jar Jar blunders through life with light-hearted good humour in spite of his occasional panic attacks.

Jar Jar is reticent about the reason for his exile from Otoh Gunga, glossing over the fact that he accidentally flooded most of Boss Nass's mansion and several adjoining bubbles while working as a waiter at a high-class party. As this was not Jar Jar's first serious accident, or even his first serious flooding accident, Boss Nass was furious, and Jar Jar was exiled from his own city under pain of death.

Jar Jar is well known to the city patrol of Otoh Gunga, which has extricated him from all kinds of trouble in the past – from petty squabbles over food theft to the commotion Jar Jar caused when he inadvertently opened half of the Otoh Gunga Zoo bubbles. They know Boss Nass will not be pleased to see the infamous Gungan in his chambers again.

*Partially retractable eyestalk*

*Nictitating membrane*

*Nostrils seal underwater*

*Large teeth for cracking shellfish*

*Tough skin near head for burrowing*

*Haillu (earlobes) for display*

*Tight vocal cords produce high-pitched voice*

*Lanky build from life in exile*

*Mottled skin for camouflage*

*Fashion statement*

*Mollusc and gumbol breakfast*

*Four-fingered hand*

GUNGAN HANDCUFFS

*Cartilaginous skeleton is stiff but not brittle*

When Qui-Gon Jinn goes to Mos Espa in search of hyperdrive parts, Jar Jar accompanies him. Qui-Gon knows that this odd Gungan will help him blend into the diverse population of strange life forms inhabiting the city. Meanwhile, Jar Jar worries about exposing his amphibian skin to the heat and suns.

_Cesta_

_Determined warrior stance_

## General Jar Jar

Boss Nass misinterprets Jar Jar's connections with the newly-favoured Naboo royalty as maturity and makes him a general in the Gungan Grand Army – much to the dismay of the troops he is to 'command'. Jar Jar lives up to their expectations when he panics during combat, falls off his mount, and instantly surrenders when surrounded. Fortunately, few soldiers pay the new general any attention and, since the Gungans win the battle anyway, Boss Nass is none the wiser.

_Castoff stretchy Gungan trousers_

_Spongy kneecaps_

_Powerful calf muscles for swimming_

### DATA FILE

◆ Jar Jar's insatiable curiosity frequently lands him in trouble. He comes close to learning a permanent lesson when he catches his tongue in Anakin's Podracer engine binders.

◆ Jar Jar speaks a pidgin Gungan dialect of Galactic Basic. Few Gungans speak the pure Gungan language.

_Tough, stubby feet_

_Tight trouser ends keep out swamp crawlies_

_Navigation sensor field indicator_

_Yaw steer indicator_

_Yaw thrust indicator_

_Main thrust indicator_

_Cockpit hydrostatic bubble_

_Starboard cargo bubble_

SUB MONITORS

_Organic Gungan design_

_Electromotive drive fins_

## Gungan Sub

Panicky Jar Jar is possibly the worst navigator the Jedi could have as they make their way through the underwater passages that connect Otoh Gunga to the Naboo capital city, Theed. He has paid no attention to submarine piloting or to finding his way beyond his swamp home. To make matters worse, Jar Jar is petrified of deep-sea creatures lurking in the caverns.

When hungry, Jar Jar eats nearly anything without a second thought, a habit learned from being exiled in the Naboo swamps. In Mos Espa market, he tries to steal a bite from a street vendor hoping that his long tongue will make short work of the morsel.

# The Gungans

GUNGANS EVOLVED in the swamps of Naboo, becoming almost equally well adapted to life on land and in water. The amphibious beings live in underwater cities hidden in deep lakes, breathing air or water with their compound lungs. Secret techniques allow Gungans to 'grow' the basic structures of buildings and vehicles, which are complemented and finished by Gungan artisans in organic styles. Gungans trade with the Naboo for certain items of technology, but manufacture everything else they need from the resources of their underwater habitat. Although Gungans use mechanized vehicles, they have a close affinity with the natural world and still prefer to utilize living mounts and beasts of burden.

*Older Gungans have hairlike finlets*

*Whiskers indicate maturity*

## Captain Tarpals

Kaadu patrol chief in Otoh Gunga, Captain Tarpals is usually on the lookout for thieves or dangerous water creatures that might threaten the Gungan populace. To the weary Tarpals, accident-prone Jar Jar Binks is a familiar menace who occupies his own special category.

*Hydrostatic bubbles of Otoh Gunga*

*Kernode assembly for larger bubbles*

*Hydrostatic field*

*Field utanode assembly*

*Utanode*

*Atmospheric purifiers*

*Minimal utanode construction requires high power draw*

*Root counterphase array*

*Backup generator*

*Stabilizer*

*Portal zone*

*Generators*

*Field wave stabilizer*

*Utanode assembly brace*

*Habitation floor*

*Counterphase harmonizing struts*

## Otoh Gunga

The magical gleam of Otoh Gunga is hidden in the deep waters of Lake Paonga. Powerful hydrostatic membrane fields keep water out of the dwelling bubbles and give the city its characteristic jewel-like look. Special portal zones hold air in and allow Gungans to pass through without needing to use an airlock.

*Field focusing element*

*Hydrostatic field generators*

## Scalefish

A variety of small fish coexist in the waters around Otoh Gunga. They are drawn to the city by its lights, but have learned by experience not to pass through to the air-filled interior.

*Poison spine*

RAY

TEE

LAA

FAA

MEE

SEE

_Mangana aqua jewel_

_Crown of rulership_

_Prosperous face_

_Epaulettes of military authority_

# Boss Nass

Ruler of Otoh Gunga, the largest lake city, Boss Nass is a stern, old-fashioned Gungan who speaks Galactic Basic with a strong accent. He commands great authority even in communities beyond Otoh Gunga and has grown large and prosperous in his advancing years. It is in Boss Nass's power alone to summon the Gungan Grand Army, which is made up of Gungans from all settlements.

_Swirl designs typical of Otoh Gungan clothing_

_Four-fingered hand_

_Rep hood_

_Rep robe_

A fair but stubborn ruler, Boss Nass resents the arrogance of the Naboo, who regard Gungans as primitive simply because they do not embrace a technological lifestyle. He finds it best all round to minimize contact with humans.

_Otoh swirls_

_Long coat denotes social importance_

_Golden coat clasp_

# Rep Teers

Boss Nass makes decisions with the assistance of his Rep Council. This group of appointed officers is responsible for various areas of government. Their special clothing indicates the dignity of their office. Rep Teers is responsible for the power supply that sustains the hydrostatic bubbles of Otoh Gunga.

Like all the Naboo, Queen Amidala was taught to think of Gungans as barbarians. But when the planet is faced with invasion, she realizes that her people and the Gungans must work together or die. Humbly finding the courage to ask Boss Nass for help, Amidala forges a new friendship between the two cultures. Deeply impressed with her gesture, Boss Nass changes his views as well.

_Gungan sandals_

## DATA FILE

◆ Boss Nass has the distinctive green skin and hooded eyes of the old Ankura lineage that hails from an isolated swamp village. His distant ancestors united with the Otolla Gungans who founded Otoh Gunga.

◆ Keeper of ancient records, Rep Been knows the secrets of old Gungan hiding places.

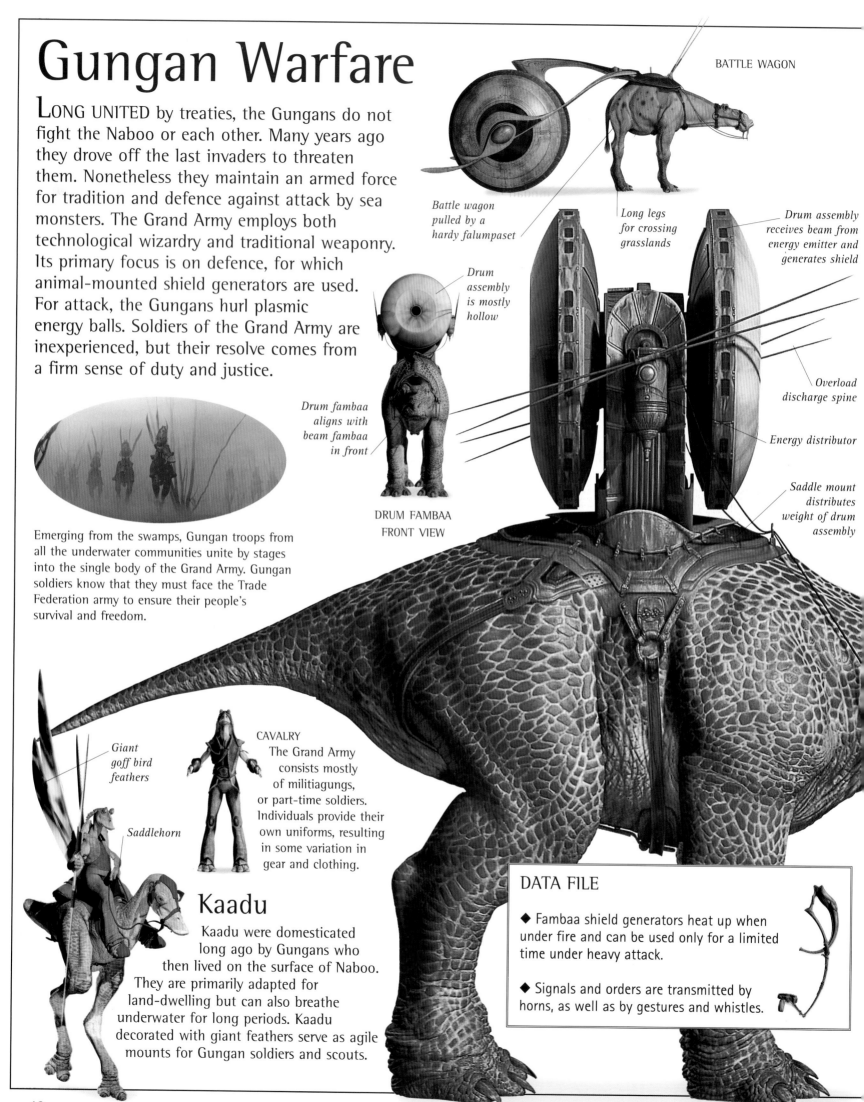

# Gungan Warfare

LONG UNITED by treaties, the Gungans do not fight the Naboo or each other. Many years ago they drove off the last invaders to threaten them. Nonetheless they maintain an armed force for tradition and defence against attack by sea monsters. The Grand Army employs both technological wizardry and traditional weaponry. Its primary focus is on defence, for which animal-mounted shield generators are used. For attack, the Gungans hurl plasmic energy balls. Soldiers of the Grand Army are inexperienced, but their resolve comes from a firm sense of duty and justice.

Emerging from the swamps, Gungan troops from all the underwater communities unite by stages into the single body of the Grand Army. Gungan soldiers know that they must face the Trade Federation army to ensure their people's survival and freedom.

BATTLE WAGON

*Battle wagon pulled by a hardy falumpaset*

*Long legs for crossing grasslands*

*Drum assembly receives beam from energy emitter and generates shield*

*Drum assembly is mostly hollow*

*Overload discharge spine*

*Energy distributor*

*Drum fambaa aligns with beam fambaa in front*

DRUM FAMBAA FRONT VIEW

*Saddle mount distributes weight of drum assembly*

*Giant goff bird feathers*

CAVALRY
The Grand Army consists mostly of militiagungs, or part-time soldiers. Individuals provide their own uniforms, resulting in some variation in gear and clothing.

*Saddlehorn*

## Kaadu

Kaadu were domesticated long ago by Gungans who then lived on the surface of Naboo. They are primarily adapted for land-dwelling but can also breathe underwater for long periods. Kaadu decorated with giant feathers serve as agile mounts for Gungan soldiers and scouts.

DATA FILE

◆ Fambaa shield generators heat up when under fire and can be used only for a limited time under heavy attack.

◆ Signals and orders are transmitted by horns, as well as by gestures and whistles.

40

Tensioner coil

Tensioner brace

Missile firing arm

Transportation wheel

Energy balls are variously sized for particular weapons

CATAPULT

Tough hornweed construction

Oil magnifier lens

FARSEEIN
(GUNGAN BINOCULARS)

Charged organic matrix contains unstable energy

ENERGY BALL

Energy ball mount

WHISTLE

## War Tools

Gungan ammunition consists of a strange form of highly destructive plasmic energy that bursts upon impact. These energy balls are prepared in different sizes and are hurled into the air by a variety of long and short range throwing sticks, simple catapults ... and occasionally by accident.

ATLATL

Broadcast power generates similar effect to fambaa shield

ENERGY SHIELD

Electrically isolated operator cockpit

Overload discharge prongs

CESTA

Shield energy emitter

Ion feed sostor

Static energy accumulation vanes

Cockpit

### CONTROLLING THE SHIELD
An insulated cockpit at the front of the shield generator assembly protects operators from dangerous electrical energy. From here they direct the generator beam towards the projector drum.

Heavy musculature

Waterproof skin

Saddle mount strap

Pillar-like legs keep high-energy shield projector well above army height

Reins

Bridle harness reinforces obedience

## Fambaa Shield

Pairs of giant fambaa swamp lizards carry the Gungans' shield apparatus. A shield energy emitter mounted on the forward fambaa fires into the projector carried on the fambaa behind, producing a spherical shield-effect impervious to almost any bombardment. The Grand Army is protected inside this shield.

Multiple Gungan fambaa shields unite to form an enormous defensive bubble. However, the shield is not impervious to slow-moving enemy troops and the Trade Federation battle droids soon break through.

# Sea Monsters of Naboo

THE WATERS OF NABOO are rich with life, the balance of sunlight and nutrients being ideal for many life forms. Microscopic plankton flourish in prodigious numbers, supporting a food chain that reaches its peak in giant predators. The sea monsters of Naboo are primarily lurkers of the deep, but some are known to drift to the surface at night or during storms – making ship travel a proverbially bad idea on the planet. Some of these monstrous creatures have been known to prey upon Gungan cities in oddly coordinated attacks, which is partly why the Gungan army stands in continued readiness. Repellent fields keep the leviathans away from the cities most of the time, but for still unexplained reasons one occasionally swims through.

*Tail highly sensitive to movement*

*Luminescent skin patterns help lure prey*

*Newborn colo claw fish are fully-equipped instinctive hunters*

BABY COLO CLAW FISH

GUNGAN SUB TRAVELLING THROUGH THE CORE

*Organs of unknown purpose at end of tail*

*Long tail provides propulsion*

*Rayed tail flukes*

*Lure*

*Jet propulsion vents*

*Pectoral fins for guidance*

*Multidirectional eyestalks*

*Tough body plates*

## Opee Sea Killer

A bizarre amalgam of traits ordinarily found only in a range of disparate creatures, the opee sea killer clings within dark crags, using a lure on its head to draw the attention of potential prey. It then pursues the prey using a combination of swimming legs and jet propulsion. The opee sucks in water through its mouth and emits it through openings under the plates in its skin, allowing strikingly fast swimming speeds. When the prey is near enough, the opee shoots out its long, sticky tongue.

*Gungan Sub*

*Tail legs drive water and help the opee cling motionless in rocky crags, waiting for prey*

Opee sea killers are both aggressive and persistent. Even when attacked by large predators, these ferocious killers refuse to give up, and young opees have been known to chew their way out of a colo claw fish's belly.

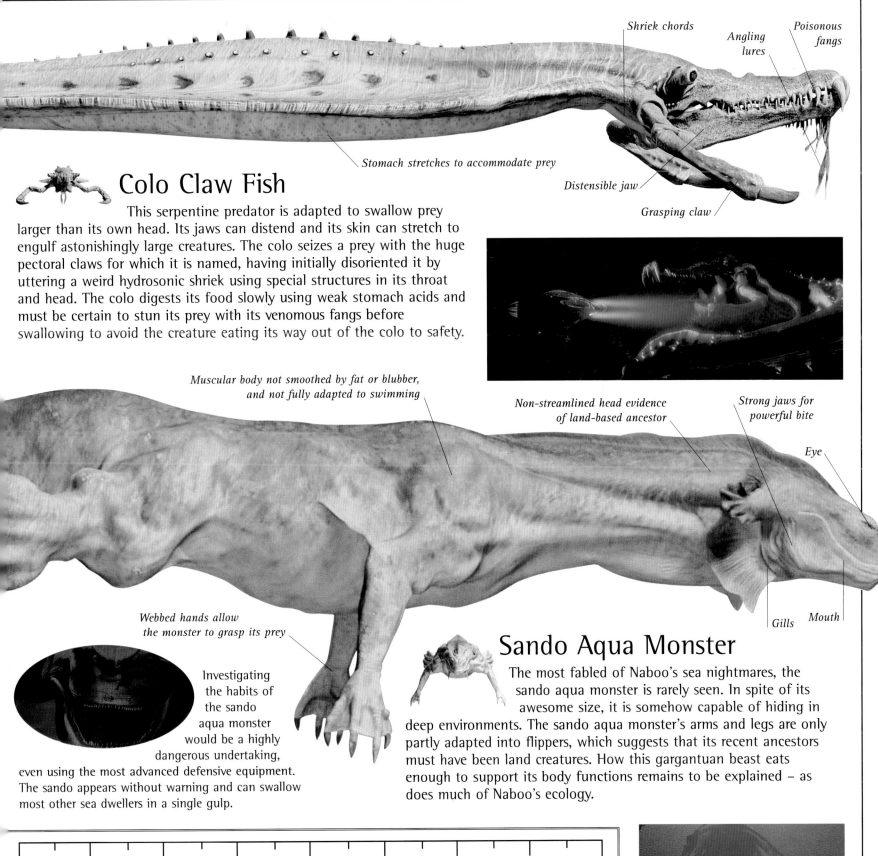

*Shriek chords*

*Angling lures*

*Poisonous fangs*

*Stomach stretches to accommodate prey*

*Distensible jaw*

*Grasping claw*

## Colo Claw Fish

This serpentine predator is adapted to swallow prey larger than its own head. Its jaws can distend and its skin can stretch to engulf astonishingly large creatures. The colo seizes a prey with the huge pectoral claws for which it is named, having initially disoriented it by uttering a weird hydrosonic shriek using special structures in its throat and head. The colo digests its food slowly using weak stomach acids and must be certain to stun its prey with its venomous fangs before swallowing to avoid the creature eating its way out of the colo to safety.

*Muscular body not smoothed by fat or blubber, and not fully adapted to swimming*

*Non-streamlined head evidence of land-based ancestor*

*Strong jaws for powerful bite*

*Eye*

*Gills*   *Mouth*

*Webbed hands allow the monster to grasp its prey*

Investigating the habits of the sando aqua monster would be a highly dangerous undertaking, even using the most advanced defensive equipment. The sando appears without warning and can swallow most other sea dwellers in a single gulp.

## Sando Aqua Monster

The most fabled of Naboo's sea nightmares, the sando aqua monster is rarely seen. In spite of its awesome size, it is somehow capable of hiding in deep environments. The sando aqua monster's arms and legs are only partly adapted into flippers, which suggests that its recent ancestors must have been land creatures. How this gargantuan beast eats enough to support its body functions remains to be explained – as does much of Naboo's ecology.

SCALE
1 CM = 100 M

GUNGAN SUB

OPEE SEA KILLER

SANDO AQUA MONSTER

COLO CLAW FISH

The opee sea killer's armoured body protects it against most underwater predators, but it is defenceless against the powerful jaws of giant leviathans such as the sando aqua monster.

# Darth Maul

FUELLED BY THE AGGRESSIVE energies of the dark side, the Sith order began almost two millennia ago with a renegade Jedi who sought to use the Force to gain control. Both strengthened and twisted by the dark side, the Sith fought against each other to gain power and domination until only one remained: Darth Bane. To prevent internecine strife, Bane remade the Sith as an order that would endure in only two individuals at a time. Biding their time, the Sith lay in wait for the right moment to overturn the Jedi and seize control of the galaxy. The present Sith Master, Darth Sidious is the diabolically brilliant mind behind the training of one of the most dangerous Sith apprentices in history: the deadly Darth Maul.

Darth Sidious uses a clear and powerful hologram transmission to communicate with his Neimoidian minions and his apprentice field agent, Darth Maul. Fiercely demanding of high standards, Sidious has been known to dismiss individuals simply for communicating with too weak a signal.

*Transmission antenna*

*Scan-absorbing stealth shell*

*Magnetic imaging device*

*Thermal imager*

*Primary photoreceptor*

*Levitator*

*External weapons mount*

*Light-gathering lens*

*Multi-scan controls*

*Power cells*

## Electrobinoculars

On Tatooine, Maul uses electrobinoculars to search for the Jedi. These electrobinoculars are equipped with radiation sensors for night vision and powerful light-gathering components for long distance scanning.

*Memory stores 360° horizon view*

*Filters screen out atmospheric interference*

*Nav-grid can be projected onto landscape*

*Alarm signals energy sources or visual targets*

*Mode indicator*

*Magnification*

*Range to target*

## Probe Droid

Darth Maul uses elaborate technology in his work as the Sith apprentice of Darth Sidious. One of his most useful tools is the 'dark eye' probe droid, a hovering reconnaissance device that can be programmed to seek out individuals or information.

ELECTROBINOCULAR VIEWSCREEN
Tied to global mapping scanners in his starship, Maul's electrobinocular viewscreen displays the precise location of targets and indicates life signals or power frequencies. Specific shapes, colours or energy types can be set as targets, and even invisible defensive fields can be detected.

Maul prides himself on his abilities as a tracker, and relishes the challenge of difficult assignments given to him by his Sith master.

'DARK EYE' DEVICES
Probe droids locate their quarry using multispectral imaging and many kinds of scanning. The probes silently monitor conversations and eavesdrop on electronic transmissions, and can be fitted with a number of small, deadly weapons.

*Scanning lens attachment*

*Ball detonator*

*Braking pedals*

*Acceleration handgrips*

*Steering bar*

*Open cockpit design offers optimum visibility*

Darth Maul's speeder is powered by a strong repulsorlift engine for rapid acceleration and sharp cornering. The open-cockpit design allows Maul to leap directly from the speeder into battle.

SITH SPEEDER
The speeder carries no weapons, since Maul prefers the direct assault of blade weapons or the treachery of bombs to the use of blasters.

*Repulsorlift*

*Vestigial horns*

*Hairless skull*

*Face tattoos*

*Gleaming yellow eyes*

# Sith Apprentice

Darth Maul is one of the most highly trained Sith in the history of the order. Focusing on physical and tactical abilities, Maul serves his master obediently, knowing that his own time for strategic wisdom and eventual domination will come. His face is tattooed with symbols giving evidence of his complete dedication to discipline in the dark side.

*Dark robe*

*Blade projection plate*

*Activator*

*Control lock*

*Blade modulation control*

*Control lock*

*Gauntlets*

*Double-bladed lightsabre*

*Beam emitter*

*Field cloak cut to allow fighting movement*

*Maul's weapon is two joined lightsabres*

*Ribbed handgrip*

*Blade modulation circuitry*

*Lightsabre blade is red due to nature of internal crystals*

*Heavy-action boots*

With his double-bladed lightsabre, Maul is equal to two Jedi who are unprepared for his powers. Since the Sith disappeared almost 2,000 years ago, Jedi are not used to facing opponents with lightsabres.

*Transmission and reception antenna*

*Function controls*

WRIST LINK
Darth Maul's programmable wrist link allows him to remotely direct 'dark eye' probe droids, arm traps, detonate bombs and conduct other treacherous activities. It also receives signals from surveillance devices.

# Maul's Lightsabre

Pushing his physical and Force-assisted abilities to the utmost, Darth Maul built and uses a double-bladed lightsabre as his primary weapon. Traditionally used only as a training device, the double-ended sabre can be much more dangerous to its wielder than an enemy. In the hands of Darth Maul, however, it becomes a whirling vortex of lethal energy.

## DATA FILE

◆ Maul's lightsabre contains two sets of internal components; one can act as backup to the other.

◆ Darth Maul's Sith Infiltrator spaceship is equipped with a rare cloaking device, allowing him to travel invisibly.

# Anakin Skywalker

ALTHOUGH HE MAY LOOK like any other nine-year-old boy living on the Outer Rim desert planet of Tatooine, Anakin Skywalker is far from ordinary. A slave to the junk dealer Watto, Anakin lives with his mother in the spaceport city of Mos Espa. He has a natural ability with mechanical devices, quickly understanding how they work. In his spare time, Anakin repairs and builds machines, including Podracer engines and a working droid. Qui-Gon Jinn notices his keen perception and unnaturally fast reflexes, and recognizes that the Force is extraordinarily strong in Anakin.

Adjustable goggles

Connection plate

Headphones

Leather neck wrap

PODRACER POWER CELL

No human has ever needed a Podracing helmet in Mos Espa, since humans ordinarily cannot ride Podracers. Anakin's extra-small helmet was made for him as a gift by Taieb, a local craftsman.

Protective magnifier eyeplate

WELDING GOGGLES

Necklace given to Anakin by his mother

Slave's simple haircut

## Family and Friends

Anakin's mother, Shmi, believes in Anakin and encourages him in his dreams to escape slavery on Tatooine. His best friend, Kitster, is a fellow slave who hopes someday to become a majordomo for a wealthy Mos Espa estate. Anakin's unusual talents sometimes distance him from his friends, but Kitster has always been loyal.

Anakin has his own room in the Skywalker home. Electronic and mechanical components are piled around his bed since Anakin is constantly tinkering and trying to figure things out. Working for Watto gives Anakin opportunities for picking up scrap equipment here and there.

Arm wraps

## Slave and Dreamer

Anakin has been raised by his mother to believe in himself. She has given him faith in his dreams in spite of their humble situation as slaves. Anakin looks forward to the day when he will be free to pilot starships of the mainline through the spacelanes of the galaxy. He soon finds that belief in one's dreams can have powerful results.

Rough work clothing

KITSTER

Among Anakin's friends is Wald, a young Rodian who speaks Huttese. Wald doubts Anakin's extraordinary abilities.

Tool pouch

Survival flares for use in sandstorms

Leg wraps keep out sand

Cheap, durable jumba leather

TRAVEL LUGGAGE

WUPIUPI (TATOOINE COINS)

## DATA FILE

◆ Anakin once belonged to Gardulla the Hutt, but she lost him in a bet to Watto when Anakin was about three years old.

◆ As a nine-year-old boy, Anakin would never be allowed to compete in civilized Podraces, but the Outer Rim is known for its exciting free-for-all race policies.

Air scoops act as
steering brakes

Radon-Ulzer
engines

Thrust
stabilizer cone

Control cable

Control Pod

*Repulsorlift*

Display
screens

# Podracer Engineer

Anakin understands the workings of Podracers from
helping mechanics and pit droids repair them for Watto.
When Anakin took a repaired Podracer for a test spin,
Watto was furious, but he was also amazed at the boy's
reflexes. Soon, the test drives turned into
qualifying laps, and Anakin became a Podracer
pilot despite his age.

*Streamlined
tail*

Anakin has secretly restored
and rebuilt a junked Podracer.
When Qui-Gon Jinn arrives in
Mos Espa, Anakin races in his
own Podracer for the first time.

*Racing graphics painted by
R2-D2 under C-3PO's direction*

*Streamlined air scoop fender*

*Power-cell
access
hatch*

*Control
linkage brace*

*Throttle
levers*

*Pilot's
seat*

*Telemetry
transmitter*

*Hydraulic pressure charging system*

*Schematic view of
engine mid-systems*

*Pressure
management
mode indicator*

# Starfighter Pilot

One of Anakin's dreams is to become
a starfighter pilot, and he practises in
simulator games whenever possible. Most of
Anakin's friends think his dreams are unrealistic, but
a few people realize that there is something special
about him. During the invasion of Naboo, Anakin
hides in a starfighter cockpit half-knowing that he
might try it out … just a little.

*Acceleration rate
indicator*

*Interval
velocity scale*

*Highlighted
system near
critical level*

ANAKIN'S PODRACER DISPLAYS

*Overpressure
alarm*

When the starfighter autopilot
engages, the ship flies Anakin
into the heart of the battle
raging above. He must think
furiously fast to figure out the
controls before he is killed.

When his dreams start coming
true faster than he can keep up,
Anakin finds himself standing in
the centre of the Jedi Council
Chamber on Coruscant. Yoda
believes that the boy is too old,
angry and fearful to begin Jedi
training. But Anakin is determined
not to be underestimated.

Crash-landing deep within the
Trade Federation Droid Control
Ship, Anakin accidentally fires
his torpedoes into the pilot
reactors, setting off a
cataclysmic chain reaction.

# Shmi Skywalker

WHEN PIRATES CAPTURED her parents during a space voyage in the Outer Rim, young Shmi Skywalker was sold into slavery and separated from her family. During a difficult childhood, Shmi was taken from one system to another by several masters of various species while serving as a house servant. When no longer a girl, Shmi was dropped from house servant status and forced into cleaning work. Although slavery is illegal in the Republic, laws do not reach all parts of the galaxy – and while inexpensive droids can perform menial tasks as well as humans, living slaves give great status and prestige to their owners.

*Simple hairstyle typical of servants*

WORKSTATION
When Shmi is not working at Watto's home, she is permitted to clean computer memory devices to bring in a modest income. A small area in their home where Shmi keeps her tools and equipment is devoted to this activity.

*Rough-spun tunic withstands harsh Tatooine weather*

*Decorative belt*

SHMI'S KITCHEN
In spite of their poverty, Shmi works hard to make a good home for herself and her son, Anakin. Her kitchen includes some labour-saving devices, but lacks the more costly moisture-conserving domes and fields, which help save precious – and expensive – water.

## Aeromagnifier

Some of the tools at Shmi's workstation were given to Shmi in recognition of her service as a dependable servant. When Watto obtained an aeromagnifier in a batch of used goods, he gave it to Shmi even though he could have sold it. The magnifier hovers in the right position to help her see what she is working on.

*Repulsor hood*

*Mladong bracelet*

*Illuminator rings*

*Magnifier*

*Spicy ahrisa*  *Lamta*  *Haroun bread*  *Sidi gourd*

MOS ESPA PRODUCE  *Tezirett seed*  *Driss pod*

## Slave and Mother

Tantalized several times by the false possibility of freedom, Shmi now accepts her life and finds joy in her son Anakin, whom she loves dearly. Shmi and Anakin live together in the Slave Quarter of Mos Espa, a collection of adobe hovels piled together at the edge of town.

When the Jedi Master Qui-Gon Jinn recognizes Anakin's special qualities and offers to take him away to a greater destiny, only Shmi's selfless care for her son gives her the strength to let him go.

### DATA FILE

◆ Shmi learned her technical skills under a former master, Pi-Lippa, who planned to grant Shmi her freedom. However, when Pi-Lippa died Shmi was sold to a relative.

◆ Shmi can always sense when Anakin is nearby, even when she cannot see or hear him.

# C-3PO

STANDARD CYBOT GALACTICA protocol droids
have been in use for generations. When Anakin
Skywalker found the structural elements of a droid
that had been scavenged for parts, he restored
it as a helper for his mother. Over time,
Anakin scrounged the parts to
complete his droid, fabricating many
components and wiring sets himself.
Anakin's droid lacks a 'skin' since
usable droid plating is valuable
and the boy cannot afford it.
The hapless droid, which
Anakin calls C-3PO, has yet
to realize that all
his parts are showing.

Balance gyro

Borrowed
photoreceptors

Vocoder
plate

Movement
sensor wiring

Photoreceptor
mount frame

Composite image
integrator

Image signal transmitter

Signal
component
collector pins

Image
component
lines

Photoreceptor
modulation
impulse carrier

Active sensing elements

Photoreceptor elements

PHOTORECEPTOR
FRONT VIEW

## Photoreceptor

The old droid frame Anakin
started with had burned-out
photoreceptors. Anakin switched
these for the eyes of a used
droid bought by Watto – which
can now barely see. Watto still
hasn't figured out how the half-
blind droid managed to walk
into his shop in the first place.

Rack for micro-tools

TOOL DEMAGNETIZER

Component schematic plans

### ANAKIN'S TOOLS
On Tatooine, many devices
are ruined by sand and dust
and then thrown away.
Anakin and Shmi look out
for such castoffs, which they
use in their work at home.

DIAGNOSTIC
SCREEN

Main power recharge socket

Pelvic
joint

Flexible mid-body
section

Magnetic
rotation
assembly
links to
actuating
coupler

While Anakin has tinkered with small
devices for years, C-3PO is his first
fully functional droid. Building a
droid, even from standardized
components, can be a challenge.

Lubricant
circulation
conduit

Auxiliary
lubrication
system
pressurizer

High-torque
knee joint

HIGH-TORQUE MOTOR

Rotating pin
anchors into
limb

Sturdy mount
pole

MICRO-CIRCUIT
WELDER

Welding
stylus

Cleaner/
energizer

## DATA FILE

◆ Most of C-3PO's structural framework is
more than 80 years old.

◆ C-3PO's programming includes memory banks
that he draws upon to design the racing graphics
for the cockpit of Anakin's
Podracer. When he works
on Anakin's machine,
Threepio teams up with
his future counterpart,
R2-D2, for the first time.

Intermotor
actuating
coupler

Structural
limb strut

Foot angle
sensor

# Watto

*Fast-beating wings allow Watto to hover*

SHREWD AND POSSESSIVE, Watto is the owner of a parts shop in the Tatooine frontier town of Mos Espa. A flying Toydarian with rapidly-beating wings, Watto's pudgy body is not as heavy as it looks due to his spongy, gas-filled tissues. The junk dealer has a sharp eye for a bargain, and knows equipment merchandise inside and out. Success has allowed Watto to indulge his passion for gambling. He regularly places large bets on Mos Espa's famous Podrace competitions, matching his wits and money against the Hutts, who control the gambling world. In the past, such bets have won Watto many slaves—prized possessions and trophies of his acumen.

In the rugged frontier society of the Outer Rim, only hard currency counts. When Qui-Gon shows up hoping to pay with Republic credits, Watto only laughs.

*Security codeout*

*Credit algorithm memory stripes*

REPUBLIC CREDIT CHIP

SERVING COUNTER TEST PANELS

## Watto's Junkshop

Although Watto insists that his establishment is a parts dealership, everyone else calls it a junk shop. It cannot be denied that the range of merchandise runs from desirable rare parts and working droids to unusable scrap that he would have a hard time unloading even on desperate Jawas. Watto's droids, slaves, and staff perform repairs, obtain parts needed by clients, and do custom work with a wide range of mechanical devices.

*Old-style sales register device*

*Protocol droid (missing some parts)*

*Miscellaneous scrap stuck to short-range re-grav plate in ceiling*

*Pit droid*

*Power droids handy for powering up depleted cells in merchandise*

*Rough adobe walls hide coolant circulating layers*

*Hard memory cycler (cleaned by Shmi Skywalker)*

*Illuminated counter surface*

*Electrostatic damping floor mats keep sand and dust down*

*Monocular photoreceptor*

*Equipment interface panel*

Bizarre improvised equipment can be found in Watto's shop, such as the Jawa R1-type drone that assists with shopkeeping.

*Serving arms*

*Diagnostic hookup for testing trade merchandise*

*Cipher converter module*

*Charger plug*

*Touch keys*

*Data read-out screen*

WATTO'S DATAPAD
Watto has an amazing memory for the inventory of his shop, but is careful to maintain accounting records in a special cipher using a sturdy datapad.

## Power Droid

Power droids of the GNK series are mobile generators that supply power for machinery or other droids. They hover silently in the background, so commonplace that they are hardly noticed.

*Monochromatic photoreceptor*

*Polyfeed power outlets*

*Ambulation gear housing*

*Vocoder*

TALKING MAGNETITE CLEANER

**Three-fingered hand**

**Dubious squint**

**Flexible trunk-like nose**

**Three-day stubble**

## HIGH-OCTANE HOVERING
Watto's wings can beat as fast as ten times a second, burning up huge reserves of energy. To fuel his intense body functions, the Toydarian eats concentrated foods and imported egg-seeds.

### DIRTY DEALING
Watto is not above using loaded chance cubes to give him an edge in his bargaining. He rolls his cubes to decide which slave to give Qui-Gon Jinn – Anakin or his mother, Shmi. However, the Jedi plays a loaded game, too, using mind powers to force the cube to favour Anakin.

**Algae-scented waistcoat**

**Belt straps**

**Keycodes for main safe and slave keepers**

**Pudgy belly mostly composed of gas**

### AT THE RACES
A favourite diversion of Watto's is watching Podraces from his fine seating box at Mos Espa Grand Arena. Nonhuman friends and acquaintances fill the box with passionate race-fan enthusiasm, as well as the vain prayers and curses of any gambling crowd.
It is the thrill of the races and the society of like-minded enthusiasts that keep Watto firmly at home on Tatooine.

**Datapad**

**Adjustable pocket welding torch**

**Odour vaporizer**

## Toydarian
The food-rich muck lakes of Watto's homeworld are filled with grabworms and other predators, making the ability to hover valuable for survival. When a safe landing is assured, Toydarian webbed feet spread out to make walking over slushy algae mats easier.

**Welding tips and brazing bars**

**Welding torch power cord**

**Refill cap**

**Solution reservoirs**

### THE GOOD LIFE
Watto enjoys smoking from a shisha oil-pipe, which mottles his skin and makes it even baggier. He uses scenters to recreate on Tatooine the algae-mat ambiance of Toydarian lakes.

## DATA FILE

◆ When he first settled on Tatooine, Watto hung out with Jawas, picking up stories and legends of great scrap finds in the desert – as well as crafty ways to sell faulty pit droids.

◆ A firm but fair master, Watto treats his slaves more decently than most.

**Mouthpiece**

**Webbed feet**

WATTO'S SHISHA

SCENTER

### LOSING
Boasting to friends of his colossal bets, Watto sets himself up for a disastrous loss when his favourite Podracer, Sebulba, loses the Boonta Eve event. What really infuriates Watto is the thought of the astronomical sums he could have won if he had bet on the winner, his own slave, Anakin Skywalker.

# Sebulba

Among the Podracer Pilots of the rugged Outer Rim circuit, Sebulba has accelerated his way to the top with an unbeatable combination of courage, skill and outrageous cheating. His murderous tactics often bring his competitors down in flames, but he knows where the race cameras are placed and manages to avoid being seen. In spite of his crimes, Sebulba has found that in Mos Espa success makes its own rules. Now enjoying the power and prestige of being a top racer, the unscrupulous Dug has just one thorn in his side — the young Podracer named Anakin Skywalker.

Sebulba's anger towards Anakin stems chiefly from fear. If the young human were ever to win a race, even by accident, Sebulba would be disgraced. The hateful Dug intends to make sure this never happens.

Sebulba is an arboreal Dug from Malastare. Swinging from tree to tree on this high-gravity planet has made Dugs strong and well coordinated. Most have no desire to leave Malastare – and this is fine with the rest of the galaxy since Dugs are notorious bullies.

Split-X radiators

Concealed flame emitter weapon

Combustion chambers

Boost afterburner

Massive engine nozzles

Control cables

Repulsor 'threader' helps Podracer avoid obstacles

Control Pod

Compressor

Sebulba's race graphics

Stabilizing vane

## Sebulba's Podracer

Sebulba's giant Collor Pondrat Plug-F Mammoth Split-X Podracer would be classified as illegally large if race officials were ever able to take a close enough look at it. Concealed weapons like Sebulba's flame emitter lend that special winning edge during a race.

Podracer cockpits are customized to suit the particular driver's anatomy. Sebulba's complex array of control pedals and levers is woven into an even more complicated automatic data transmission bank that provides read-outs of all engine conditions during the race.

The race crowds love a winner, and Sebulba delivers victories time and again. The odious Dug plays to the crowd when in their sight, and has become the heavy favourite in the betting pits.

Main combustion pyrometer readout

Pre-feed pyrometer readout

Throttle lever

Aeration mix gauge

Second-stage fuel flow rate indicator

Crowd-pleasing grin

Wattle

## Sebulba, Podrace Anarchist

Sebulba is highly skilled Podracer, but he was not quite good enough to make it to the top on ability alone. When he found that intimidation and race violations were quite effective in gaining victory, he refined these abilities and began to add secret weapons to his racing machine. Dispatching opponents without getting caught is now the chief sporting aspect of Podracing for the malevolent Dug.

Lekku head-tails

Blue skin characteristic of Rutian Twi'leks

Slave collar

SECRET WEAPONS
Whether jamming the engine telemetry of his opponents or planting faulty probes among their pit tools, Sebulba is a competitor to be reckoned with.

Parafrequency modulators

Charge handle

SENSOR FREQUENCY JAMMER

Short-range antenna

Intake bellows

Sampling analyzer (sabotaged)

Activator pommel

REACTANT LEAK SNIFFER

Race cap over sagittal crest

Race goggles

Ear fins

Beaded danglers

## Twi'lek Twins

Sebulba hates the Hutts, but has learned a thing or two about how to spend money from attending their parties. The vile Dug has recently purchased expensive blue Rutian Twi'lek twins as masseuses, partly to put him in best form for the race but mostly to irritate his fellow racers and steep them in jealousy. The tactic has been resoundingly effective.

Tromin form-fitting unigarment

Former hind limbs adapted as primary manipulators

Loose neck skin inflates during mating calls

Grasping hands

Padding for rough turns

Leather racing outfit

Backrest

Bowl seat

Leather wrist guard

LUCKY CHAIR
The exotically built Dugs are uncommon in the galaxy so they have difficulty finding comfortable chairs. Sebulba paid a Mos Espa furniture maker to construct a massage chair for him, which he now considers to be 'lucky'.

Limbrest

## Sebulba

One of Sebulba's first purchases with a major victory-prize purse was a leather racing outfit. This flashy costume was custom-made to suit his particular anatomy. Much more decorative than functional, the banded style nonetheless suits the Dug's chosen image and is popular with his toughest and most violent fans. Sebulba hangs coins from each race victory prize onto his costume as decorations and wearable trophies.

Trophy coins

Former front limbs adapted into legs

Tight leather leg-straps

## DATA FILE

◆ Sebulba's Podracer has a top speed of over 829 kph (515 mph).

◆ One of Sebulba's earliest Podracer weapons spat a stream of nails into the faces of racers coming up behind him. He has since switched to a secret flame emitter.

# Podrace Crews

PODRACERS are complex machines that require extensive maintenance and frequent repair. The mechanical stress of running high-performance engines at up to 800 kilometres per hour takes a heavy toll on any Tatooine Podracer. The pit crews rebuild the battered machines and prepare them for the next big race. Assisted by frantic pit droids and pestered by race officials citing violations, Podracer crews must also put up with the egos of the racers themselves. In spite of it all, the crews take great satisfaction in knowing that they make all the action possible.

*Harmonic sensor*

*Alignment screen*

*Rectifier scale*  *Output sampler*

POWER OUTPUT ANALYZER    INSTRUMENT CALIBRATOR

Podracing crews use specialized instruments to analyze engine performance and diagnose faults. Tools should be standardized for safety and fairness, but in practice no two crews have the same gear.

*Overhead crane track*

*Heavy cranes move Podracer engines*

*Skylights muted with cloth*

*Massive Podracer engines*

*Lubricant hoses provide many kinds of oil*

*Reactant pressurizers*

*Pit droid*

*Power cell chargers*

*Sebulba and his slaves on display*

## Pit Hangar

In the huge Podracer hangar at Mos Espa Grand Arena Podracers are tuned to their best by busy pit crews until the last minute before a race. Heavy-duty overhead cranes help with maintenance and repair. Race officials attempt to certify the vehicles, but the crews use every tactic imaginable to distract, threaten or bribe them.

*Multi-frequency power impulse detector*

*Carrying strap*

*Signal clarifier*

*Receiver antenna*

*Low-frequency enhancer*

*Handle*

*Impulse detector unit*

*Impulse probe tip*

IMPULSE DETECTORS
Key parts of every pit mechanic's kit are impulse detectors, which monitor the dangerous power outputs of Podracers.

*Polarizing field insulator*

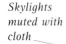

The mammoth, deafeningly loud turbines of Podracer engines require fine-tuning to make it through a race. The delicate work can often be dangerous, and mechanics must be careful when they are near the engines whether they are ignited or not.

*Pacithhip mechanic*

*Utility tool vest*

*Welding goggles*

PODRACE MECHANICS
Humans, who cannot safely pilot the blindingly fast Podracers, often become expert mechanics in Podracer crews. These largely unsung geniuses build some of the best engines for species that can exploit the powerful machines to their fullest capacities.

Pit droids are such a common sight near Podracers that they go mostly unnoticed, in spite of the bizarre antics they sometimes engage in when trying to get a job done. The real mechanics are left to make the complex decisions and oversee customized engine modifications.

*Ion baffles*

CURRENT
FLOW FILTER

*Vanadium alloy*

*Insulating sleeve*    *Firing terminal*

PODRACER POWER PLUG

*Droid intercommunication antenna*

*Head plate protects against falling tools*

*Monocular photoreceptor*

*Hardened alloy casing*

*High-torque motors for strength*

*Smooth universal joint*

*High-output power source needs frequent recharging*

*Tough construction*

# Pit Droids

Programmed to have a permanent sense of urgency, pit droids are utility mechanics that assist with Podracer maintenance jobs. Their compact form allows them to reach small parts and linkages in and under the big engines. Pit droids are built with minimal logic processors so they take orders without asking personal or superfluous questions. However, this also leaves them easily confused and apt to get into trouble when left to their own devices.

## THE MAIN PODRACER CONTENDERS

*Internal cycling ring circles pilot seat*

**TEEMTO PAGALIES**
Proud of his new cycling-electromagnet stabilizer, Teemto Pagalies is entering his barely tested Podracer in the Boonta Classic, believing that it will give him the winning edge.

*Energy-binder plate*

*Massive turbine intakes*

**RATTS TYERELL**
Although he looks harmless, Ratts Tyerell has a quick-change metabolism that gives him lightning reflexes in the heat of a Podrace – or on the run from predatory sagcatchers on his homeworld.

*Anti-turbulence vanes*

**GASGANO**
With his 24 fingers, Gasgano can perform several tasks at once, including balancing Podracer fuel feeds, controlling the pressure valves and optimizing the reactant mix in the engines.

*Thrust stabilizer cone*

**BEN QUADINAROS**
Used to Podracing in the Pouffra Circuit, Ben Quadinaros is nearly petrified with fear at his first race in the famously dangerous Boonta Classic on Tatooine.

*Quad-control cables*

*Core fuel tank*

# The Podrace Crowd

NOTHING COMPARES to the sheer spectacle of Podracing as witnessed in the worlds of the Outer Rim. Racers tear through rugged landscapes driving all manner of non-standardized machines in a contest of raw nerve and razor-edge calculation. Each racer has fought blistering competition to get on the circuit, rules are seen as guidelines and safety concerns are thrown to the wind. To witness an all-star event like the Boonta Eve Podrace on Tatooine is to live the thrill of racing at its most intense.

Race course through desert wilderness — Pit hangar — North stands — Starters' box and finish line

*Arena citadel with betting floors*

*Concessions concourse*

*Starting grid*

*Shuttle terminal*

*West stands*

*Patches repair damage from being shot down*

*Jawa-built envelope*

*Cheap channel race omnicam*

SIDE VIEW

*Transmission antenna*

*Repulsorlift wing*

*Multiple lenses catch a range of angles on key turns and speed flats*

PODRACE CAM DROID

## Mos Espa Arena

The atmosphere before a Podrace is electric. Spectators take their seats in the stands; the rich enter their boxes or elevating platforms for an aerial view; Podracers are prepared in the pit building and the betting floors are scenes of feverish activity as the odds are updated every few seconds.

The starters' box holds race officials, the starting light and three lap indicators.

*Starting light* — *Lap indicators*

*Parade of racers' flags*

The system for determining the starting lineup of the Boonta Eve race involves an apparently baffling combination of performance statistics, outright bribery and sheer chance.

FLOONORP

SABRIQUET

DRIXFAR

Race cameras used to be built into the rocks along the course to help spectators catch every thrill, but these were all stolen or shot to pieces. Now, a fleet of hovering cam droids is used.

FANATICAL SPECTATORS
Thousands of race fans fill the vast capacity of Mos Espa Grand Arena for the big races such as the Boonta Eve. Every language in the galaxy is heard from the Podrace enthusiasts as entire fortunes are wagered on current favourites and hopeless longshots.

MUSICAL INSTRUMENTS
Musicians stroll the stands on race day, entertaining the crowds for contributions. Many of the improvised instruments they play are made from engine parts.

## DATA FILE

◆ Mos Espa Arena holds more than 100,000 spectators.

◆ Race contestants are granted seating for chosen supporters. Anakin's mother and friends watch the race from an elevating platform.

- *Double ballonets inside envelope for stability*
- *Supporting framework*
- *Tibanna gas compound keeps balloon afloat*

## Podrace Balloons

The Hutts charge fans to use viewscreen channels supplied by official repulsorlift race cameras. However, a gray market of cheap channels fed by balloon cameras has sprung up, since only permanent and repulsorlift-powered cameras are controlled. Some brave spectators even watch the race from rented balloons, which are often shot down by drunk and disorderly fans or angry losing betters.

- *High tensile-strength cables*
- *Spectator gondola*
- *Stereo-view double eyepieces*
- *Channel select*
- *Display mode select*
- *Grip bars*
- *Motion-tracking scanner*

**HAND-HELD VIEWSCREENS**
Giant screens in the sumptuous levels of the Arena Citadel betting floors monitor the views from the race cameras. However, most fans prefer to to watch the race in the stands using rented screens or electrobinoculars.

**RACE ELECTROBINOCULARS**

## THE PODRACERS

*Poor-quality welding*

**BOLES ROOR**
Racing his near-stock Podracer, Boles Roor is out of his league on Tatooine, where they don't make allowances for sub-par skills. He will be lucky to finish the race.

*Racing ensignia*

**MARS GUO**
A loudmouthed braggart, Mars Guo is a Phuii with a chip on his shoulder and an eye for blue masseuses in skimpy outfits. Guo will find that it doesn't pay to chat up a Dug's slave girl when the Dug is a fiend for revenge.

- *Triocular vision*
- *Neural bundles process sensory input at high speed*
- *Electrostatic repeller visor*

| MAWHONIC | ARK "BUMPY" ROOSE | NEVA KEE | ELAN MAK | CLEGG HOLDFAST |

- *Thermoregulator flaps*

| ALDAR BEEDO | EBE ENDOCOTT | WAN SANDAGE | DUD BOLT | ODY MANDRELL |

## Jabba the Hutt

Somewhere in Mos Espa there is a little-known official who legally rules the city, but the wealthy gangster 'First Citizen' Jabba the Hutt is really in control. Jabba presides over the Boonta Eve race from the best box seats in the arena, thinking only of the profits he will reap through his gambling organizations. His major-domo Bib Fortuna attends to every arrangement, keeping Jabba's entertainment running as smoothly as his criminal operations.

- *Jabba the Hutt*
- *Bib Fortuna, Jabba's Twi'lek major-domo*
- *Diva Shaliqua, one of Jabba's slaves*
- *Jabba's shisha*
- *Chokk, an armed bodyguard*
- *R5-X2 computes betting odds and Jabba's winnings*
- *Huttese glyphs of good fortune*
- *Diva Funquita, Gardulla's assistant*
- *Gardulla the Hutt, Jabba's guest and sometime rival*
- *Dwarf nunas brought back by one of Jabba's assassins from a recent mission*

# Tatooine Inhabitants

A FRONTIER WORLD, the desert planet Tatooine lies on an important hyperspace route between the civilized planets of the galactic core and the distant star systems of the Outer Rim. Traders and smugglers run all manner of goods through Tatooine's spaceports, answering to few authorities besides the gangster Hutts. On the desert surface, inhabitants include desperate settlers, impoverished spacers, aliens of dubious reputation, droids of all kinds, along with the scattered representatives of Tatooine's native populations, who are best adapted to life on this difficult world.

The slave Erdan was chemically enlarged by his owner to increase his work-rate. His face was patterned as a mark of ownership.

Spacers willing to run routes into the risky areas beyond Tatooine wait for work in a streetside café, where cooled table slabs offer some respite from the heat. Games like triga help to pass the time.

*Drann player markers*

*Sett player home*

**TRIGA GAME**

*Spacers' café*

*Cheap imitation chiller tables offer no coolth*

*Teguar deal-maker*

*Retractable awning*

*Amphibious gorgs cooked at street stalls*

*Non-indigenous species recovered from freighter bilge*

*Locals keep a low profile*

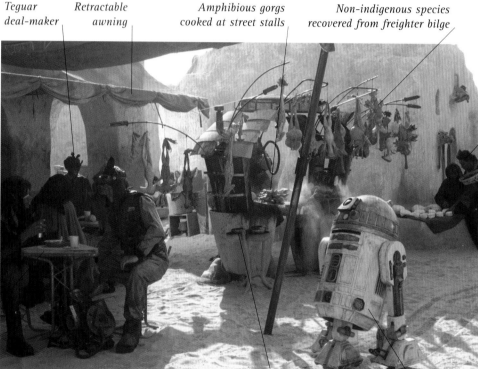

*Gorg dipping sauces*

*R2-D2*

## Marketplace

In the crowded marketplace alleys of Mos Espa, various quarters specialize in particular types of trade. Some serve the day-to-day needs of local inhabitants, while others house droid mechanics, engine repairers, and – if you know where to look – illegal weapons dealers.

*Broken antenna*

*Welding droid*

*Head salvaged from Temirca droid*

*Intensity controls*

*Compressor*

*Montoro serving drone body*

*Coolth emitter vents*

*Repair worker arms*

**COOLING UNIT**
Many street vendors in Mos Espa keep cooling units near their wares to draw potential customers from the hot streets.

*Podracer engine shroud*

**GORGMONGER**
Gragra claims to keep her amphibian food stock in a large basement culture pool, but she actually grows them in a sewer zone under Mos Espa.

## Droids

In the Outer Rim, ancient and heavily repaired droids can often be seen lurching through back alleys. Also common are exotic hybrids made of parts combined from dissimilar droids. The resulting machines tend to have either limited mentalities or personalities as bizarre as their origins.

Ignored or derided by the gangster and spacer classes, Mos Espa settlers try their hardest to avoid involvement in local disputes or gunfights.

**Suspicious-looking luggage**

**White skin pigmentation reflects sunlight**

# Beasts of Burden

**Scaly skin retains moisture**

Tatooine's heat, dust and sandstorms can damage mechanical transport, but animals make ideal beasts of burden. Dewbacks are used all over Tatooine, eopies are common only around Mos Espa, and banthas are the exclusive mounts of the Sandpeople.

DEWBACK

**Flexible snout for uncovering sand lichen that grow just beneath the planet surface**

**Gaffi stick**

**Long barrel for accuracy**

**Broad feet for sand travel**

EOPIE

**Sandproof bindings**

**Stolen projectile rifle**

**Protective eye lenses**

**Filtering sandmask**

Natives of Tatooine, eopies are able to carry heavy loads in intense heat without tiring.

**Bound hands**

**Heavy cloak and bindings protect against sand and sun**

**Ammo bandoleer**

At times, sandpeople steal guns but strongly favour traditional club and axe weapons for close quarters combat.

**Clan-crafted leatherwork**

Indigenous to Tatooine, Jawas have become used to contact with space travellers. Many Jawas act as metal scavengers and equipment-repair craftworkers.

**Sling**

**Power cell**

**Long robe allows free movement and ventilation**

Sandpeople take pot shots at fast-moving Podracers from remote sections of the Podrace course, hoping to strand and attack race pilots.

BACKPACK COOLERS
Twin suns make for searing hot middays, so pedestrians in Mos Espa often wear personal cooling units.

## DATA FILE

◆ Jawa clans can be distinguished by subtle differences in their cloak designs.

◆ Children in Mos Espa play with fortune-telling 'Eyes of Mesra', an old desert tradition.

# Sandpeople

Unlike the Jawas, the native Tatooine Sandpeople have not adapted to easy contact with outworld settlers. Resentful of incursions in their territory, Sandpeople prey upon travellers and are known as Tusken Raiders. Renowned for their savagery, Tusken Raiders are lethally dangerous and not to be trifled with.

**Handle**

**Ion charger exhaust**

**Collector**

**Intake**

SANDSTAT
Sand and dust blows into every corner of Mos Espa; the fastidious clean up with electrostatic sandstats.

**Bandaged feet**

# Chancellor Valorum

*Distinguished gray hair*

*Premature ageing from pressures of governing*

*Veda cloth robe*

*Ornate overcloak*

A LIFETIME OF PREPARATION led to Finis Valorum's election as Supreme Chancellor of the Galactic Senate. Valorum inherited the legacy of a family whose greatest members had each represented more than 1,000 worlds. Centuries ago, a Valorum served as Supreme Chancellor. Finis Valorum has now equalled this achievement, ruling the entire Republic from the galactic seat on Coruscant. However, he has also inherited a government grown weak from its own success: the galactic representatives have become distanced from their people and now the entire system is degenerating.

## Coruscant

The galactic capital, Coruscant, is almost entirely covered with skyscrapers. These kilometres-high buildings provide living space for more than a trillion inhabitants, including the thousands of representatives in the Senate Chamber. The planet is entirely dependent on outside support to survive, consuming resource shipments from a steady stream of vast freighters.

*Blue band symbolic of Supreme Chancellor*

## Sei Taria

*Septsilk robe signifies wealth*

Chancellor Valorum's administrative aide, Sei Taria assists him in confirming the fine details of necessary procedural regulations. She has learned much from Senator Palpatine.

*Chagrian horns used for intimidating display*

*Blue skin screens out harmful radiation*

*Lethorns*

## DATA FILE

◆ Coruscant has been the centre of galactic government for tens of thousands of years. Its early history is shrouded in legend.

◆ Increasingly, Supreme Chancellor Valorum has been influenced by senators such as Palpatine to compromise what he knows is right for the sake of approved procedure.

## Mas Amedda

The stern Chagrian Mas Amedda is responsible for keeping order in the Senate. Accused of misusing his parliamentary powers for bribes, Amedda stands firm to his own code of honour.

## AIR TAXIS

*Multi-spectrum headlights*

*Communications antenna*

Air taxis carry passengers throughout the bewildering maze of canyons and pinnacles in Coruscant's skyscraper landscape.

*High altitude repulsors*

# Senate Guard

The guards of the Galactic Senate wear striking robes of blue, symbolizing the Senate's supreme authority and the long tradition of its wise and just rule. The large crest and simple drape are ceremonial effects rather than functional designs.

*Highly visible crest*

*Muzzle brake dampens rifle blast*

*Large, unwieldy ceremonial rifle*

*Platform seating*

*Senate guard*

## SENATE PLATFORMS

The vast amphitheatre of the Senate Rotunda is lined with 1,024 platforms. The majority are used by sectorial senators, who represent their own planet and hundreds of others in a galactic sector. The remaining platforms are available for limited periods to alliances, commercial powers or individual planets with special causes to bring before the senate.

*Repulsorlift*

HOVERCAM
SIDE VIEW

When a senate representative is recognized for official speech, their senate platform detaches itself from the rotunda and flies out into the open chamber for prominence.

*Rodian representative on senate platform*

*Control antenna*

# Hovercam

A squadron of flying hovercams patrols the Rotunda to record the speeches and votes of the Senate representatives. Some hovercam operators abuse their responsibility and omit to record certain individuals, while others allow unscrupulous senators to alter the record of their words after they are spoken.

*Wide angle lens*

*Telephoto lens*

*Repulsor floaters*

## THE DIVERSITY OF THE SENATE

A vast range of alien species populates the Senate Rotunda, hailing from every corner of the Republic. Among them can be seen the traditional costumes of hundreds of planets, as well as many fashions particular to Coruscant.

*Alderaan aides*

*Dual mouths for stereo language*

*Brain in neck hump*

SENATOR
YARUA FROM
KASHYYYK

LIANA
MERIAN

AGRIPPA
ALDRETE

TENDAU BENDON

Renowned for their tempers, Wookiee senators are nonetheless possessed of a firm sense of fair justice. Senator Yarua finds commercial power within the senate reprehensible and is determined to restore justice to galactic government.

*Blue colour hints at Palpatine's interest in the Chancellorship*

*Elaborate cloak asserts sectorial authority*

# Senator Palpatine

ENDLESS PATIENCE has been Palpatine's key to success. Passed over as a young politician and repeatedly turned down for office and appointment, he has learned the value of quiet persistence. Palpatine has risen through the ranks to attain the powerful office of sectorial representative to the Galactic Senate on Coruscant. Palpatine represents some 36 worlds in a backwater sector, of which his provincial home planet of Naboo is typical. Turning this background to his advantage, Palpatine has been ever-present in the halls of galactic politics, impressing friend and opponent alike with his unassuming demeanour and simple but powerful insights into how the galaxy could be better run.

Over time Palpatine has developed a reputation as someone apart from intrigue and corruption, as he patiently condemns the many abuses of bureaucracy that come to his attention. It is little surprise to insiders that he is nominated for the office of Supreme Chancellor.

*Palpatine's apartment is modest compared to the stunning palaces of other sectorial representatives*

PALPATINE'S APARTMENT Few outsiders are welcomed into Palpatine's scarlet chambers. They are the exclusive haunt of his trusted confidants until Amidala arrives for the first time on Coruscant.

*Queen Amidala*

*Naboo-style bloused sleeves with long cuffs*

*Royal handmaiden*

*Strange red decor*

## Diplomat

Palpatine never favoured Naboo's previous sovereign, King Veruna, even after the stubborn ruler heeded Palpatine's suggestions to become more involved in foreign affairs. Queen Amidala suits Palpatine, since he believes she will better follow his directions.

Before they meet at the Senate, Queen Amidala has only seen Palpatine in person once, at her coronation. She half-suspects that his concern for Naboo is secondary to his political ambitions.

### DATA FILE

◆ Senator Palapatine's unusual choice of art objects reveals to Queen Amidala that he has left his Naboo heritage far behind and has adopted a more worldly point of view.

ROUTE TO SUCCESS Palpatine consistently favours less concern for senatorial legality and procedure and more attention to simply doing what he considers needs to be done. It is as

a result of this practical attitude that many look forward to the clear-minded leadership that Palpatine promises to provide.

# The Senate

THE POWER of sectorial senators is immense, as they control access to the Senate for hundreds of planets. The temptations that go with such power are equally great. Corrupt senators are no longer unusual, even at the highest level, and few Republic citizens expect anything but empty promises and word games from anyone who sets foot on Coruscant. In truth, many senators are simply lazy and greedy, but by doing nothing to stop the spread of evil they become some of its greatest supporters.

*Gesture showing objection*

*Gesture denying guilt*

*Gesture blaming others*

*Gesture of reassurance*

MOT NOT RAB

BASKOL YEESRIM

PASSEL ARGENTE

HOROX RYYDER

## SENATORIAL POLITICS

Many senators have become known for judicious nonalignment, allowing their worlds to profit from supplying both sides in conflicts. Critics comment that three-eyed Malastarians like Baskol Yeesrim can not only see both sides of an issue, but can always spot their position of advantage right in the centre.

*Over-indulgent features*

*Ear flaps store fat*

*Lekku (head-tail)*

*Rare red-skinned Lethan Twi'lek*

*Gaudy robe*

## Consorts

Senators are attended by assistants, aides and consorts according to customs and traditions of their home planets and sectors. Many young aides are repulsed by the abuses of government they see on Coruscant, but they stay on, reluctant to lose their positions of power.

CONSORT TO TOONBUCK TOORA

Senator Toonbuck Toora's last traces of idealism have been eradicated by watching the downfall of the just and from counting the profits that flow from finding loopholes in the law. She now counts as friends criminal senators she once held in contempt and rewards loyal supporters with well-paid appointments as consorts or aides.

## Senator Orn Free Taa

Indulgent lifestyles are nowhere more extreme than on Coruscant. Senator Orn Free Taa has found possibilities beyond his wildest dreams. He views galactic government as merely the sport of the mighty like himself. In his excesses he has grown vile and corpulent, but he is confident that money and power will always make him attractive.

## DATA FILE

◆ Lavender was chosen for the colour of the Senate interior because it was the only hue that had never been associated with war, anger or mourning in any culture in the Republic.

◆ Senator Tikkes moved from business to Coruscant politics to make some *real* money.

*Protective racing goggles*

*Racing cap*

*Long neck to peer above vegetation mats*

*Extremely fast reflexes used for evading carnivorous trap branches and swarms of deadly challat eaters*

*Secondary manipulative arms normally hidden under clothing for decorum*

*Long limbs allow spider-like movement through caves and up giant trees*

*Primary manipulator arm*

GASGANO

www.starwars.com     www.dk.com

**PROJECT ART EDITORS** Iain Morris & Jane Thomas
**PROJECT EDITOR** Simon Beecroft
**US EDITOR** Sarah Hines Stephens
**MANAGING ART EDITOR** Cathy Tincknell
**MANAGING EDITOR** Joanna Devereux
**DESIGNERS** Kim Browne & Guy Harvey
**DTP DESIGNER** Jill Bunyan
**PRODUCTION** Steve Lang
**US PICTURE RESEARCH** Cara Evangelista
**US PHOTO LIBRARY** Tina Mills
**ILM IMAGE COORDINATOR** Christine Owens

First published in Great Britain in 1999 by
Dorling Kindersley Limited,
9 Henrietta Street, London WC2E 8PS

2 4 6 8 10 9 7 5 3 1

Copyright © 1999 Lucasfilm Ltd. & ™.

A CIP catalogue record for this book is available from the British Library

ISBN 0-7513-7057-6

Colour reproduction by Colourscan, Singapore
Printed in China by L. Rex Printing Co.

# Acknowledgements

Many hands made this book possible, and the Captain would like to express special thanks to a few in particular:
Ty Teiger and his prop department at Leavesden Studios fabricated the amazing range of marvellous guns and gadgets filling these pages to overflowing; the book is also a parade of the sumptuous and extraordinary costumes created by costume designer Trisha Biggar and her team; special additional fabrication was provided by ILM modelmaker Don Bies, who cracked open the battle droid head for us; Ed Maggiani and Steve Cymszo made sure that even the most diminutive Jedi Master had a custom-made lightsabre; design consultant Iain Morris somehow managed to be multiple persons at once, and one or two of him helmed the outstanding layouts herein that would make even text copied from a phone book look brilliant; art editor Jane Thomas joined us at Skywalker Ranch to provide vital help, making possible the completion of the book design in a fortnight or so (give or take); David Pickering's sage editorial influence still hovered over my keyboard like the spirit of Obi-Wan; but when I was prepared to keenly regret his absence, DK editor Simon Beecroft appeared courageously to offer (along with lots of editorial work) crucial good cheer, stimulating conversation, and the editorial encouragement that makes really satisfying work possible; Lucasfilm editor Sarah Hines Stephens also stepped in for

this book with a smile and a keen eye, keeping the evolving backstories in harmony with the rest of the *Star Wars* universe; charming Lucas Licensing Publishing Coordinator Cara Evangelista provided great stacks of reference material to the team from the beginning, when there was chaos and the darkness was without form; all this imagery was forged at the anvils of Image Coordinator Tina Mills, who must have a separate universe in her office and a large supply of invisible extra assistants to accomplish what she and her staff do; FBI Special Agent R. Matthew Bliss offered the benefit of his expertise in refining the secret profile of Darth Maul, marking what was probably the first time a U.S. federal agent has professionally explored the background of a Sith Lord; chief engineer George Stephens Whitcomb, formerly of the U.S. Navy nuclear aircraft carrier CV-66 *U.S.S. America*, was, as always, an inspiration in speculative functionality; poet, thief, and swordsman extraordinaire Jack "Tony" Bobo, Esq., provided immeasurable assistance in firing my imagination, as did treasure hunter and writer Carl "Ray the Barbarian" Cart, whose fiction is concentrated like nitroglycerine and who sets the high standard toward which I strive; Prof. Gregory S. Aldrete, Ph.D., of the History department at the University of Wisconsin at Green Bay, offered ongoing conversations on the links between society, art, artifacts,

and culture, which influence my entire approach to interpretative analysis, even in the *Star Wars* universe; Hugh Quarshie contributed one of the most interesting discussions I enjoyed during all my time on the film sets at Leavesden, including his privileged insight into the intrigue within the Naboo royalty; Neal Porter and Fiona Macmillan at DK were a pleasure to work with and kept me proud of the team I was on; Lucasfilm US editor Jane Mason helped the book take shape in its earliest stages; Lucasfilm Director of Publishing Lucy Wilson stuck with me and my unusual circumstances for another rewarding project; and finally, Ann Marie Reynolds offered me support throughout and proved the value of her editorial influence on yet another project, making sure that Simon didn't see anything that was *really* first draft.

DK Publishing would also like to thank:
Alex Ivanov and David Owens for additional photography; Justin Graham, Scott Carter, Matthew Azeveda, Paloma Añoveros, Susan Copley, Danielle Roode, and Fay David for additional research; David John for additional editorial work; John Kelly and Mark Regardsoe for additional design work.